In This Strange Soil

Jillian Hensley

Levellers Press

AMHERST, MASSACHUSETTS

In This Strange Soil is a work of fiction set against a background of historical events. The characters whose stories play out in this context are products of the author's imagination. Any resemblance to persons living or dead is coincidental.

Published by *Levellers Press*, Amherst, Massachusetts

Printed in the United States of America

ISBN 978-1-937146-99-3

For Peter,
who is always there for me

CONTENTS

In This Strange Soil

Preface

Shortly after arriving in Westborough, Massachusetts, from South Africa in January 1979, I was exploring our new neighborhood when, at the entrance to the high school, I came across a rock on which there was a plaque with this inscription:

In the field south of this spot
August 8 1704
Indians killed Nahor
and captured Ashur, Adonijah,
Silas and Timothy Rice

These words haunted me. Why were these people kidnapped? How old were they? Did anyone try to rescue them? What happened to them after they were captured? Who were the captors and why did they kill Nahor? When I discovered that the captives were children, I was determined to find out more about them. This story grew out of my research and my imagination.

Jillian Hensley
May 2016

Madrid, Spain

In a darkened room of El Escorial, fetid with the nostrums of physicians and the incantations of exorcists, King Charles II of Spain was dying. Generations of Habsburg inbreeding had left him weak of intellect as well as body, and he had no heir. As courtiers and healers hovered about the moribund monarch, he suddenly roused himself and demanded to be taken to the family crypt. There, to the horror of the assembled grandees, vaults were opened that he might gaze upon the embalmed remains. When the tomb of his first wife revealed the French princess whose life was cut short by the stifling Spanish court and the ministrations of its doctors, Charles broke into uncontrollable weeping and was led back to his room. There, under the tutelage of the cardinal archbishop of Toledo, he made a will naming as heir to the Spanish throne Philip of Anjou, grandson of Louis XIV.

Despite the best efforts of doctors and exorcists, Charles II died at the age of 39 on November 11, 1700.

When the contents of his will became known among the crowned heads of Europe, consternation reigned. England and Holland, in particular, were concerned at France's growing commercial strength. A French king on the throne of Spain was an unacceptable expansion of Louis XIV's already far-reaching power. Thus it was that two years after the death of Charles II much of Europe was engulfed in the War of the Spanish Succession. The Atlantic Ocean was no barrier to these hostilities, and the fledgling colonies of France and England in the New World soon found themselves embroiled in the ancient enmities of the Old.

TOURAINE, FRANCE

In the dim glow of dawn in early January, 1703, a modest chateau on the outskirts of the French city of Tours becomes visible against a somber sky. Glimmers of candlelight, first at one window, then another, finally come to rest in the casement beside the dark slab of the door. As pale rays pierce the clouds, touching the stone façade and mansard roof, the sound of hooves on icy ground breaks the serenity of the winter morning. A groom leading two horses comes into view from behind the building. As they pass the lighted window, the door opens, and a tall figure in the black habit of a Jesuit stands silhouetted in the entry. Turning his head, he says in a low tone, "The horses are here, Étienne. We must leave soon if we are to be in time for the diligence. *" Indicating to the groom that they will shortly be departing, he closes the door.*

Within the tapestried hall, a woman stands beside the marble mantel, a blazing wood fire emphasizing the fine planes of her face and her deep-set eyes. Despite the early hour, Aurélie de Surville is fully dressed. A young man in the uniform of one of the king's cavalry regiments stands before her.

"Do not be concerned for me, Étienne," she is saying. "I am happy that you have the opportunity to accompany your brother to Rennes, for only God knows when we will see him again. In the weeks that you are away, I will make preparations for my sojourn with the sisters at Fontevraud while you are in service to the king. On your return it will comfort me to have news of where he is to be sent. Vincent, dear son," she says, turning to the Jesuit, "I commend you to God. The path in life He has opened to you is a noble one."

Vincent clasps her hands. "Mother," he replies, "I will keep a faithful record of all that the Creator may consider necessary for me to experi-

ence, and send my writings here. I know that you will not be allowed to receive letters while you are at the abbey, but Étienne will bring you news of me whenever he has leave from his duties."

Then, kneeling before her, he says, "May I have your blessing to carry with me?" Head bent, he cannot see the tears as she places a hand lightly on his head. Rising, he embraces her; then waiting only for his brother to take a similar farewell he strides to the door without looking back.

LETTER ONE

THE ATLANTIC OCEAN

Aboard La Bonne Espérance, the 24th Day of April, 1703

My dear brother,

Having left Bordeaux on the tenth day of March, we have now been at sea more than a month, and I pray that when you receive this letter it will find you in good health. I am grateful that that you were able to spend time with me at Rennes before my departure, and I trust that the arrangements we put in place for our mother's care are proving to be advantageous to her.

I am profiting from a sleepless night to begin an account of my experiences and thoughts as I embark on my journey into the unknown. With God as my guide, I have no fears. I beg you to preserve these personal chronicles as modest imitations of the *Relations* of those early Jesuit missionaries whose lives so profoundly inspired mine. By immediately recording my impressions of events in my journal whenever possible, I believe such accounts will provide a limited but true perspective on life in that outpost of our empire, and my small part in it. I also hope to increase the interest and immediacy of my experiences by including conversations, as I recall them. My memory is excellent in that regard, as you know.

This call to service in the New World in my thirty-second year is the realization of my life's ardent ambition, Étienne. Do you remember when I was fifteen, my heart was filled with dreams of Marguerite Rambouillet? I know our parents, and hers, saw in our youthful infatuation the seeds of a marriage beneficial to both families. Sweet memories flow from those months of innocent dalliance, of musical soirées poignant with shy glances, of strolls with our parents through quiet avenues after church. Being twelve at the time, you will no doubt recall that in the oppressive summer of my sixteenth birthday, I fell ill with the ague. Marguerite's distress on receiving the news was pitiful. She begged our mother for permission to tend me, but her parents, fearing for her health, would not consent to her staying by my side. On several occasions in the course of the fever, delirium released in me visions of anguished souls who were denied knowledge of Christ. They rose like vapors around my bed, spectral arms groping blindly. My cries of distress would bring Mother to my bedside to soothe me with cooling draughts infused with cinchona, whereupon the ghastly visions subsided. When at last the illness left me, I vowed to wrest those lost souls from their torments. Seeking guidance in the volumes of our father's library, God led me to the words of the Jesuit fathers who first went forth into the wilderness. There, in the *Relations* of those brave soldiers in Christ, I found the inspiration for my life's work. Indeed, the strength of the feelings aroused in me by the example of those saintly men dispelled my heart's longing for Marguerite. (I still beg God's forgiveness for the pain I caused her. She could not comprehend the pure passion in my heart that left no room for any other.) In particular, the sufferings of Father Isaac Jogues, of blessed memory, revealed to me a nobility of spirit that became, and remains, my fervent yet humble aspiration. Though fiendishly tortured by the Mohawk whom he had come to save—his fingernails pulled out, his thumbs cut off, his body bruised and broken by beatings—he remained filled with the Holy Ghost. For some time he lived as a slave among the savages until, thanks to the compassion of Dutch merchants who helped him to escape this bondage, he returned to France to recuperate. The effects of his sufferings were so severe that he was unrecognizable to those who had known him. Yet, after regaining his health, the light of his faith and his love for his converts maintained his resolution to return to the scene of his agonies. Suspected of practicing magic when crops failed, he met his death by tomahawk two years later.

By the grace of God, and however humbly, I am about to follow the path that he and others hewed through the wilds of the New World and the wilderness of unbelief. I yearn to begin work among the heathen of New France, and to instruct heretics in the mysteries of our holy faith, for I was told before leaving France that many English Puritans have been captured in raids by our army and its Indian allies and taken to New France.

On my arrival in Bordeaux, and having deposited my bag at an inn, I went to the harbor to find the ship upon which I was to sail. It proved to be *La Bonne Espérance*, a three-masted barque of four hundred tons, which looked to my inexpert eye to be well-found. It was my good fortune to encounter the first mate who was supervising the loading of cargo and animals. He informed me that my fellow passengers were to be six emigrant families, numbering about thirty men, women and children, five indentured servants, and a contingent of ten soldiers. He showed me my narrow cabin below the quarter-deck, in which I could barely stand upright, and which I was to share with one of the military officers. Most fortunately, our little cell was blessed with a port-hole, a luxury denied my fellow travelers, who were to live and sleep in the gun room or in a cramped common area, three or four to a family bunk, with the light of day visible only through the ventilation grids.

Arriving two days before we were due to sail, I was pleased to have time to explore Bordeaux. Acting on the recommendation of the innkeeper, my first destination was the Tour Pey-Berland. From its summit I was able to see much of the city, which follows a crescent-shaped curve in the Garonne River that gives Bordeaux its byname, "Port of the Moon." In close proximity to my lookout, the twin spires of Cathédrale Saint André, venerated by the faithful on their long pilgrimage to Compostela, proclaimed God's glory. Before sunrise on the morning of our departure, I made my way to that noble place of worship, where I put myself in God's hands. As the dawn light filtered through the rose window, illuminating the vaulted ceiling in a fractured rainbow of colors, a priest entered by a side door and knelt before the altar. When he had completed his orison, I rose and approached him, asking him to hear my confession, which he was most willing to do. Thus fortified within my soul, I was prepared to face whatever trials God might place before me.

I hastened back to the dock, where passengers laden with bundles and baskets were filing up the gangway. They stood in subdued groups until the soldiers, who had boarded earlier, directed them to their sleeping quarters. At last the preparations were complete, and, the wind and tide being favorable, the mainmast flag was hoisted and a shot fired to announce our departure. On the captain's orders, sailors cast off the hawsers and unfurled a small sail. As our vessel moved from the dock and swung into the wind, I stood at the rail and watched the coast of France slowly fade until it no longer separated the firmament from the ocean. My heart reached out to our beloved homeland and those whom I hold dear. At that moment I knew, and accepted, dear brother, that the vagaries of my new life might prevent me from ever setting foot in the land of our birth again.

As we were informed at Rennes, my destination is the mission of Kahnawake in New France. Since coming on board, I have been reading the books I obtained at the seminary, and have learned that missionaries of our order established this settlement in 1680 as a refuge for Indians who chose to be baptized into our faith. It is situated on the great Saint Lawrence River, a five-day canoe journey southwest of Québec, which is where we will come ashore in New France. I spend many hours, too, studying the Mohawk tongue, and refining my knowledge of Huron, which is the language of prayer at Kahnawake. My work will mainly be among the Mohawk, one of the five tribes comprising the Iroquois League, the others being the Oneida, Seneca, Cayuga and Onondaga. It appears that in the distant past these peoples destroyed each other in an endless cycle of blood feuds and so-called mourning wars in which revenge was taken and slain tribal members replaced by captives to placate grieving clan mothers. At this dark time, according to their legend, Tekanawita, a mysterious Huron, appeared in the ter-

ritory of the Kanien'keha:ka (People of the Flint), as the Mohawk
call themselves. Having proved his special powers by succeeding
in challenging trials that no ordinary man could have survived,
the Mohawk were prepared to listen to, and accept, Tekanawita's
message of peace and harmony. The other tribes followed their
example, with the exception of the Onondaga. A sorcerer named
Atatahrho, whose evil was manifested in his crooked body and the
tangle of snakes that covered his head, held that nation in thrall.
His power was such that without his participation, Tekanawita's
Great Law of Peace could not prevail. A delegation from the other
tribes traveled to Onondaga. There, they recruited the noble Aion-
wátha as their spokesman. He, together with Tekanawita and the
delegation, sang a song of peace to Atatahrho, whereupon he was
released from the evil that inhabited him, leaving his people free
to join the alliance. The women, who wield great influence among
the Iroquois, then selected sachems (statesmen) from each tribe to
serve on a Great Council, and the Iroquois League came into being. They called themselves the Haudenosaunee, or People of the
Longhouse, because they envisioned this alliance as a traditional
dwelling in which the Mohawk and Seneca functioned as keepers
of the eastern and western doors, the Onondaga as preservers of
the central fire, and the Oneida and Cayuga as the younger, but
equally important, brothers. Because members of one nation could
only marry into another Iroquois nation, loyalties were established
that curbed the devastating effects of bloody strife by extending the
circle of kinship.

It is remarkable, Étienne, that savages have devised a way of living in harmony that our civilization would do well to emulate, for
under this Great Law, the participating nations swore to 'bury the
hatchet' under the Great Tree of Peace, and to defend each other
against all enemies. Further, because all people are held to be equal,
decisions are made only when all have had the opportunity to express their views and have 'come to one mind.'

Much of my time on board has been occupied in thus educating myself, and taking advantage of the many opportunities for

service. Besides celebrating Mass each morning and hearing the confessions of the faithful, I tend the sick and instruct the children.

Life proceeded peacefully in this manner until late in the afternoon of our seventh day at sea. I was reading in my cabin when I became aware of a change in the pitching of the ship. There was a tension in the air that seemed ominous to me, and I went on deck to find the vessel moving sluggishly through dark, heaving seas beneath a sky livid with menace. As I stood at the rail, the captain issued orders to reef the sails. Instantly, the crew sprang into action, responding to commands relayed from master, to first mate, to boatswain, and finally to the matelots, who scaled the swaying rope ladders to the topmost sails. As I stood marveling at their courage and skill, one of the officers stopped briefly by my side. "Heavy weather coming, Father. Say a prayer for us," he proclaimed cheerfully. A few minutes later, a wind from the northeast that billowed those sails yet to be reefed was followed by a vicious squall that whipped the sullen ocean swells into whitecaps. Driving rain forced me below deck, where all was in disarray. Beneath wildly swinging lanterns, men and women struggled to recover onions, potatoes and cabbages that scattered in every direction from overturned baskets. A barrel of salt beef that had burst free of its restraints careened from one side of the ship to the other, and mothers attempted to comfort children who had staggered into the wooden stanchions with the sudden rolling of the ship.

Yet this was but a mild prelude to the carnage to come. For the next three days, the wind tormented us with capricious gusts that veered from northeast to southwest, creating cross seas with waves that battered our ship from every direction and shook her from stem to stern. Within, what misery! Water forced itself beneath the covers of the ventilation grids and streamed down upon the bedding and clothing of those below decks. The sufferings and indignities of seasickness afflicted almost everyone, including me, and the wild motions of the ship made the use of slop buckets impossible. By the second day, the stench from the passengers' area had permeated the ship like a miasma from hell itself. My cabin mate, Lieut. Jacques Hubert, being one of those fortunates immune to *mal de mer*, did his best to alleviate my misery by moistening my lips with water, but there was nothing he could do to allay the effects of the violent motion and the noisome effluvium from which there was no escape. Thus, I lay in my bunk as miserable from my malaise as from my inability to be of assistance to those whose suffering was far more intense than mine.

And then—O blessed relief!—throughout the fourth day, the wind gradually ceased its shrieking, gusts no longer made the ship's timbers moan, the decks became stable. Some of the crew, freed from their labor of keeping the ship from foundering, were sent below decks to restore order, assisted by those sturdy passengers able to recover most quickly from their ordeal. To my satisfaction, I found I could include myself in their number, and so I set about helping the crew with their swabbing, carrying dank bedding to the deck for airing, and comforting those still confined to their bunks. By evening, the stench had been subdued by scrubbing the floor with vinegar water, and though some of those worst affected by the storm were still unable to stand or take nourishment, most passengers could move about below decks and derive strength from a large cauldron of broth provided by order of the captain.

The next morning, I ventured early on deck. The first mate had made it known throughout the ship that a service would be held at five bells in the forenoon. Accordingly, at the appointed time, the crew, and those passengers who were well enough, gathered around me on the deck. There, beneath scudding clouds that afforded glimpses of blue sky, I led them in a prayer of thankfulness, inspired by the strength and truth of Psalm 107: "God commanded, and raised the stormy wind, which lifted up the waves of the sea. They mounted up to heaven, they went down to the depths; their courage melted away in their evil plight; they reeled and staggered like drunken men, and were at their wits' end. They cried to God in their trouble, and God made the storm be still, and the waves of the sea were hushed."

I count it a blessing, Étienne, to have witnessed God's power and majesty in the fury of the storm. More than ever, I am aware that we are puny creatures dependent on His Divine Providence for our salvation. Wishing to contemplate our deliverance, and to rejoice in the clean air and the sunshine, I found a seat on a coil of rope in the lee of the forecastle later that day. The voices of matelots repairing torn sails or operating the bilge pumps beside the masts mingled with the murmurings of passengers and the laughter of children, who, though weakened by their ordeal, had emerged from below decks eager to refresh their spirits.

The 2nd Day of May, 1703

The captain has just informed me that we are within three days of Québec, the storm having blown us off course and prolonged our voyage by more than a week.

When we arrive in Québec, I hope to find a ship to carry this letter without delay to France. Pray for me as I begin my mission. You and our beloved mother are ever present in my heart and my prayers.

Yours in Christ,

Vincent, S.J.

LETTER TWO

New France

(eight months later)

Kahnawake, the 4ᵗʰ Day of January 1704

Skennen kówa ken, dear brother!

That is to say, "Do you have the Great Peace?" Spoken, it sounds like this: skanna go wa ga.

I regret that it was not in my power to reply earlier to your most welcome letter, which came into my hands three months after my arrival in the New World. Becoming accustomed to my daily responsibilities left me time only to remedy my deficiencies in the Mohawk language in order to communicate effectively with my flock. As you can see from the greeting that opens this letter, Indian language is rich in metaphor. You will I am sure recall how we labored over translations from French into English or German, as required by our tutor. Imagine then the difficulties in working with a language that in structure, syntax and vocabulary is completely alien to those in Europe! In recounting speech, I can but try to capture the essence and spirit of the Mohawk tongue.

We arrived at Québec on the fifth day of May, and, having navigated our way among a host of *navires* of all descriptions, plus a swarm of canoes, which afforded me my first glimpse of the savages who inhabit the New World, we at last dropped anchor. After so many weeks at sea, it was with unsteady legs and profound emotion that I set foot on this vast and wild continent. Being in need of respite after our long voyage, I tarried some days at our Society's seminary, which gave me time to explore this settlement of more than two thousand people. Naturally, I was particularly interested in observing the native inhabitants, who are strikingly well-made physically, being erect and proud in their carriage, strong and agile in their movements. The faces of many men are elaborately tattooed; most have heads innocent of hair except for a scalp-lock decorated with beads and feathers. The few women that I saw were modestly and gracefully dressed in deerskin robes decorated with beads and with porcupine quills dyed in vibrant colors. They wear their long hair parted in the middle and tied back with ribbon that I was told is made from eel skin.

After almost a week in the town, I was impatient to resume my journey. Five days by canoe on the Saint Lawrence River brought me to Kahnawake on the tenth day of June last year. I believe I mentioned earlier that it is situated about ten miles southwest of Montréal, and as we approached the settlement, Indians in elm bark canoes drew alongside, curious to see the new 'Black Robe.' At some distance from the stone wharf where we landed, I observed three large cannons, but a rough wooden palisade obscured the village. Having entered through a gate, all was alien to my eyes: rows of bark-covered dwellings (those longhouses so central to the Iroquois tradition), smoke rising from holes in their domed roofs; women pounding corn, making leather articles, or scraping skins before the low doors of their habitations; children tumbling in the dust or playing games with pebbles. A few young men lounged in the sun, and I was told by one of them who approached me in welcome that the majority of their comrades were away on a hunting expedition. Near a larger longhouse, which I later learned was a council chamber, some older men were gathered, greeting me courteously in their guttural tongue. Amid the strangeness, what balm to see a cross gracing the roof of a wood-framed, bark-covered building on a low rise! As I hastened toward this beacon of our faith, Fathers Jacques Lamberville and Pierre Cholonec, having received news of my arrival, came forth and welcomed me with the utmost kindness. They are men of wisdom and accomplishment who have spent many years among the Indians. Both are now more than sixty years of age, and I count myself blessed to be working with them. I pray that I may emulate their success in bringing the Word to both heathens and heretics.

Beside the simple church of Saint Xavier, with its carillon of three bells that mark the division of our days, stands the priests' modest residence overlooking the majestic Saint Lawrence River, the thunder of the Lachine Rapids at Sault Saint Louis reminding us continually of God's might. My chamber, which is six feet long and five feet wide, contains but a narrow bed, a *prie-dieu* and a crucifix.

My life, of course, centers on the church, its simplicity reflecting the tenets of Our Lord. It remains redolent of the blessed Kateri Tekakwitha, a Huron by birth, but known as The Lily of the Mohawks, whose extraordinary fervor and privations brought her perfect unity with God through prayer. She lived at Kahnawake for several years, dying in the odor of sanctity at the age of twenty-four. Her likeness, which adorns the church, was preserved by the artistic talents of our revered Father Claude Chauchetière, who, God be praised, is still with us at Kahnawake.

My work here is exalted by the saintly example of Kateri, and by that of my brother priests. From the time we rise at four o'clock in the morning, we distribute the Bread of Life to the faithful. Our days follow the same exercises as those at our houses in France, with Masses and prayers throughout the morning, which are attended by many of our flock. I find particular joy in the children's Mass, followed by a catechism class in which Father Claude's pictures and small books illustrating the creation of the world, the Passion of our Lord, and the torments of hell, explain our faith to eager young audiences.

I have now established that this village of close to one thousand souls comprises between fifty and sixty dwellings, about sixty-five feet long, twenty feet wide and twenty feet high, with a door at either end. There is a broad aisle down the center giving access to compartments, each providing space for one family, and furnished with wooden sleeping platforms covered with grass mats and furs.

Shelves above the sleeping areas provide storage for clothing, snow shoes and other equipment, while a profusion of foodstuffs is stored or suspended wherever space can be found: braided corn, dried berries, fish and meat, bark containers of bear grease and maple syrup. Such structures house up to ten families, who share open hearths beneath smoke holes in the roof.

Beyond the palisade surrounding the settlement are fields that in the growing months produce an abundance of corn, squash and beans, known as The Three Sisters among the Indians. Our mission is truly a haven where all who would join the community must forswear the evils of polygamy and drunkenness. It is to be deplored, Étienne, that for so long members of our race, who claim to be the bearers of civilization, have corrupted the Indians with drink, against which they have no natural defense. A large part of the blame must go to French, English and Dutch traders and the *coureurs des bois,* all of whom, in greedy pursuit of the beaver, or to win the alliance of one tribe or another, have fomented death and destruction among the natives for more than a century. They are agents of the Demon, arousing covetousness for the firearms and trinkets of the white man, as well as his alcohol.

My afternoons are devoted to visiting the sick, and I daily give thanks that my interest in the human body led me to pore over volumes of Vesalius and Paré in the library at the seminary. I have had to accustom myself to working with my patients in the dim light of the longhouses, where the pervasive smoke is, I believe, the cause of many of the illnesses afflicting our people.

I value these visits as opportunities to get to know our flock and learn about their culture and customs. Central to their social order are the clans, of which, at Kahnawake, there are three: Wolf, Bear and Turtle. Clan members, all of whom are descended from a common female ancestor, are regarded as kin, and marriage to a member of the same clan, no matter what tribe they belong to, is considered an abomination. I attribute our Mohawks' remarkable vigor and enviable physical development in large part to this rule. I cannot help but contrast the restraint of these so-called 'savages' with the degeneracy of the Habsburgs that is at the root of the war in which we are now embroiled. Without the generations of inbreeding among them, the Spanish king would likely have had an heir, sparing Europe and the New World their present convulsions regarding a successor to the throne of Spain.

But I digress.

As I mentioned earlier, women have significant influence in Iroquois culture. Although the Council of Elders is composed of men, it is the women who choose the chiefs and influence the councils, even in matters of war. Their bloodlines determine succession; they maintain the tribe through their authority over the fields and harvests, the longhouses and the children, the regulation of slaves and captives, and the arrangement of marriages. When a man marries, he moves into his wife's longhouse, and whatever the number of his children, his bloodline dies with him. Yet this lack of male dynastic and domestic power does not produce weaklings, but superb hunters, warriors, and statesmen.

One of the most perfect examples of the loyalty, integrity and fearlessness of a Mohawk warrior, blended with the mercy of a Christian, is Oughtzorongoughton, which I will transpose as Oserohkoton. He is the son of Ontasaga, chief of the Turtle Clan, who remains faithful to the traditions and customs of his tribe. His wife, Onatah, on the other hand, accepted the grace of baptism before her son was born. She is a model of Christian virtue who instructed Oserohkoton in the tenets of our faith from his infancy. He is now about twenty-three years of age, and many are the tales of his exploits. From his earliest years he showed exceptional physical prowess. When not more than twelve years old, he accompanied the men on a deer hunt, helping to carry supplies and set up camp at night. Game was scarce, but one day he was following the hunters when his sharp eyes discerned the silhouette of a deer in a thicket some distance from the trail. Alerting his companions, he took off at a run. Accustomed though they were to grueling chases, the men could not catch up with the boy. At the end of four hours, they found him sitting beside the body of the deer, which he had dispatched with his knife when it fell from exhaustion. The men carried the boy home on their shoulders, proclaiming his feat as they entered the village.

On another occasion, Oserohkoton, aged about fifteen, went on a spring hunting expedition. An older boy, wishing to prove his bravery, entered a cave known to be the den of an exceptionally large male bear. His inexpert spear-thrust maddened the beast, which set upon his attacker, raking his back as he tried to escape from the cave. Without hesitation, young Oserohkoton rushed forward and flung his spear, piercing the bear in the throat. Moving in for the kill, he waited until the bear stood upright, frantically trying to rid itself of the spear. Then, dodging the flailing claws, he plunged his knife into the creature's heart, escaping with only gashes on his chest—marks of honor that distinguish him to this day. He has also gained renown for his steadfastness in skirmishes with the Abenakis, who regularly make incursions into the Mohawk fishing and hunting grounds.

His courage is therefore well established. However, he is also gaining honor as an orator, a skill much respected among the Indians. Recently, I attended a council held in the large longhouse situated near our church. A young hothead of the Wolf Clan had killed a member of the Turtle Clan in a dispute over a flintlock musket. When I entered the chamber, the sacred fire symbolizing the Great Spirit, had been lit. The assembled sachems, each seated in front of delegates from their clans, were passing the ceremonial calumet in a circle from east to west in honor of the sun and praying for wisdom in their deliberations, for tobacco is considered sacred and is used in many rituals. When I had seated myself slightly beyond the circle, Ontasaga courteously invited me to join in smoking the pipe of peace. What follows is a much-condensed account of the proceedings. Because the Indians believe it is wrong for one person to impose his will on another, they take great pains, by means of summaries and repetition, to ensure that everyone has understood what a speaker has said. All is accomplished with the utmost prudence and discretion.

Ontasaga rose to speak for the Turtle Clan. "Brothers," he began, "we have assembled here in the sight of the Great Spirit to right a grievous wrong. We have discussed this matter and do not desire to insult or provoke our brothers of the Wolf Clan, who are themselves filled with shame at the conduct of one of their own. We seek only to fill the place of our kinsman honorably, and in keeping with his value to our people. Our ears are open."

The Wolf Clan leader rose to respond.

"Brothers, we have deliberated long and solemnly for we wish to atone for the blood of the slain. We offer these goods that your hearts may be healed and your labors eased."

Before the large array of valuable gifts could be displayed to the assembly, the wife of the murdered man came forward.

"Who is to provide for me and my children?" she demanded. "Where will I find meat to sustain us and skins to cover us? A life should be given for a life. This murderer is not fit to live."

The leaders consulted in low tones with their clansmen, but seemed unable to come to an agreement. Oserohkoton had been following the discussion closely. As he was not yet a chief, he was not entitled to speak in council, but he felt moved to do so. Rising, he respectfully asked permission. After murmured deliberation among the elders, he received a sign of assent from Ontasaga.

"Brothers, let us not forget that most of us are Christians," he said. "For the love of the Son of God, let we of the Turtle forgive Canawangoe for his sin against our clan. However, forgiveness does not mean that justice should not be done. You shall have a life for a life, my sister."

A low hum of surprise and apprehension rose from the gathering, for above all they wished to avoid bloodshed.

"In accordance with our tradition, the bereavement gifts honor the one who has died and comfort those who grieve. They are yours to accept," said Oserohkoton, turning toward the wronged woman. "But let us never forget that life is God's, and only God's, to take. Canawangoe is eighteen years old. I propose that he be required to provide for our sister and her family for the same number of years that he has been on this earth. During the time he is in her service, he will not be permitted to marry, and if he fails to abide by these rulings, he will be cast out of the clan to live in shame. However, should our sister at any time wish to take a man to be the father of her future children, Canawangoe will be released from the penalties imposed by this council. That is my thought on the subject. Hiro— I have said."

There was silence as the assembly considered the implications of this proposal. Then, one by one, the clan chiefs put forward their opinions for discussion. When general agreement had been reached, the chiefs and their delegations rose. In one long exhalation, they indicated their approval. "Koué," they intoned.

"It is done," Ontasaga declared. "By this we wash out the blood of the slain." Turning to the bereaved wife he asked, "Is this to your satisfaction, sister?"

"My heart is at peace," she replied.

Thus was the matter settled thanks to the sagacity of Oserohkoton.

Impressed with the wisdom and eloquence manifested in so young a man, I approached him several days later as he sat at the entrance to Onatah's longhouse fashioning a snowshoe in the late afternoon sunlight. Addressing him in Mohawk, which is now almost as familiar to me as our mother tongue, he set aside his work, and rose to greet me. I complimented him on his part in judiciously settling the dispute with the Wolf Clan, and asked whether I might sit with him for a while. With the utmost frankness of expression he gazed at me for a few moments, then entered the longhouse, emerging immediately with a cask to serve me as a seat. Taking up his work, he said, "You wished to speak with me, Father?"

"I wish to understand whence come your wisdom and your ability to weave words in such a way that your listeners see it unfold before them."

His fingers continuing to attach thongs to the wooden frame, he sat in silence for several minutes.

"From my youngest years," he said, "my father spoke of the importance of giving thanks to the Great Spirit for the return of each season, for the sun after rain, for the light of a new day, for food that gives us life and strength. Humbly we thank Him, too, for the power of speech that grants us the ability to understand our fellow humans, but does not set us above creatures who cannot speak as we do. He showed me that words must be balanced by silence, which he called the Great Mystery. For us, it is the voice of the Creator, a sacred gift that allows us to live in harmony with our selfhoods and to pass through the troubles of the world with patience, courage and dignity."

His words were a revelation to me, Étienne, for they perfectly expressed our order's concept of 'serene acceptance.'

"This wisdom accords with that of the Black Robes, my son," I responded. "May I know what brought you to accept baptism?"

"When my mother was a young girl," he said, "the piety of Blessed Kateri took root in her heart. One day, she crept silently into the church where Kateri was praying before the altar. The holy woman's face glowed with her love of God, and the blemishes from the variola she suffered as a child became invisible. It was as if He had removed a veil from before His face, allowing her to see Him in His glory. It was at this time that my mother's eyes were opened to the truth of miracles."

He told me that along with other female followers of Kateri, Onatah mortified her body to excess, depriving herself of food and driving out supposed sinfulness with scourges, hair shirts and iron girdles.

"Did none urge moderation, my son?" I asked.

"These actions caused Father Chauchetière great unease," he replied. "He declared that henceforth the women must come to him for approval of their penances. At this time, my mother's fervor was such that Father Lamberville pronounced her ready to be baptized. This sacred rite he performed when she was seventeen years old, a year before the death of Kateri. Since then, as you have seen, Father, her faith has not wavered."

I asked whether Onatah had ever considered becoming a nun, a path that some of Kateri's followers had taken in emulation of her vow of perpetual virginity. He replied that his mother did not consecrate herself to Jesus, choosing instead to marry Ontasaga.

"She saw in him a man of wisdom and honor who respected her religion. She, in turn, respected his. It was she who taught me to venerate the saints and to accept the pope as my spiritual father so that I may dwell with God in the Sky World when I leave this earth."

Placing my hand on his shoulder, I said, "Your mother is blessed for passing on God's holy Word to you, and for being worthy in every way to be called a Christian." With a smile I added, "What you have told me explains your wisdom but not your eloquence, my son."

"In that, I follow my father, who is honored for his oratory. He told me that before addressing the Council, he prepares his ears to listen and his heart to understand. That way, he said, the words find their proper place when they leave his mouth. This I have found to be true."

As the bell rang for Vespers, Oserohkoton rose to accompany me to the church. There we found Onatah already kneeling in prayer. We joined her in praising Him who is Father of us all.

One evening some days later, I was seated at an open window in our common room playing my flute when Oserohkoton passed by. He immediately came up to me, eyes alight.

"Father, I too have a waterennótha' that makes such a sound, but it receives its breath from the end, not the side. What is its name in your language?"

"It is called a flute. Come in that you may hear it better."

He entered the room and seated himself on the bench beside me, observing me intently as I played. When the music ended, he pointed to the sheet that I had been reading.

"What is the meaning of those marks, Father?' he asked.

"It is the language of music."

He looked incredulous.

"How does it tell your ...flute ... " (he stumbled over the unfamiliar word) "what sound to make?"

I showed him that the marks on the paper went up or down according to the pitch of the note. He quickly grasped the principle, and asked whether he might bring his waterennótha' sometime to learn the language of its brother flutes.

This was the first of several enjoyable and companionable interludes. On one such occasion, I looked up from reading my music to find Oserohkoton regarding me with a slight smile.

"Father, we Kanien'keha:ka usually play our flutes together with others at ceremonies. We seldom play alone except when we are courting. The first night I heard you playing I knew that circumstance could not be true for you." After a long pause, he asked, "Would you be willing to tell me why the Black Robes do not associate with women?"

"It is for the sake of the kingdom of heaven, my son. We are called to this way of life so that we may freely offer ourselves in sacrifice for God's glory when He calls us to do so. We also seek to serve the faithful with undivided hearts, seeing all within our Holy Mother Church as our children."

He pondered this for a while. "I believe that is as noble in God's sight as my wish to bring children into the world to praise Him," he said.

This young man, who is near enough to you in age, Étienne, is becoming like a brother to me. He has a natural quickness of mind and a curiosity that leads him to interrupt our musical sessions with questions about life on the other side of the Great Water. When he achieves chief's status, he will bring honor to his people and to our faith.

Our day-to-day lives were uneventful until December of last year, when news came that there was to be an assault on a New England town in which our young men would be involved. There have been many such raids. Terrorizing New England towns is part of our army's strategy to depopulate the frontier in what is known here as Queen Anne's War. In this endeavor, we French make full use of the Indian tradition of the mourning war. The savages are much affected by the death of relatives. To ease their profound sadness, they replace tribal members lost in battle or through disease by taking captives in raids on neighboring tribes. Having for more than a century been decimated by European diseases, as well as by tribal warfare, our Indian allies are desperate to recoup their losses through adoptions. In building up the strength of their tribes, English settlers are as acceptable to them as members of their own race.

Two days ago, Father Jacques Lamberville called me aside after our evening meal. He told me that arrangements are in place for an attack in February on the town of Deerfield on the English frontier. Lieutenant Jean-Baptiste Hertel de Rouville, who will be in command, has requested that a priest accompany the expedition. As my *confrères* are beyond the age for such duties, the spiritual care of the army and our Christian Mohawks will be in my hands. Father Jacques urged me to use the occasion well as it will afford an opportunity to instruct any captured heretics in the errors of their beliefs.

This is the call to service for which God has been preparing me, Étienne. May I prove worthy of His trust.

Having obtained your commission, I am aware that you, too, dear brother, are at a crucial point in your life. From your account, it would seem that the battle for the throne of Spain shows no sign of abating and that you can be called to take up arms at any time. You mention that early next year you will be joining your regiment to fight somewhere in Europe, or, possibly, in New France. God willing, we may meet on these shores. I pray daily to Saint Martin for your safety and for peace, taking comfort and pride in the knowledge that you will always bring honor to the name of de Surville whatever your destiny may be.

A courier awaits. Forgive me for leaving you and our mother so long in ignorance of my well-being.

You are ever in my prayers.

Yours in Christ,

Vincent, S.J.

Post scriptum: I depend upon you to transmit the essentials of this letter to our mother, to whom I send professions of my devotion.

New France

(FIVE MONTHS LATER)

Kahnawake, the 7ᵗʰ Day of June, 1704

Dear Étienne,

It has taken me some weeks to recover from the rigors of our journey to New England in the frigid air and deep snows of February and March.

In the third week of January, I was summoned to report to Fort Chambly on the Richelieu River at Québec, along with seventy-five of our Mohawks. Ontasaga, being beyond the age for participating in the life of a warrior, was not among them, but it pleased me to see that his son was. Our band joined fifty French soldiers and a group of about one hundred and fifty Pennacooks, Iroquois, Abenakis and Pocumtucks, these last eager to avenge the loss of their land to the English. All were in a state of high expectation, the soldiers eager for adventure and military glory, the Indians for captives and plunder. Incessant clamor assailed my ears: trumpet calls marking the divisions of the soldiers' days; frenetic throbbing calling the Indians to feasts and dances, the latter accompanied by whoops and ululations; all this cacophony punctuated by the orations of clan chiefs exhorting their followers, and promising rich rewards. The chapel was my only sanctuary, where I was gratified to find some of our Mohawks, including Oserohkoton, on several occasions. He being much involved in helping to organize preparations for the journey, our paths seldom crossed, but he took advantage of a chance meeting to present me with most welcome gifts: snow shoes of his own making, and, from Onatah, deerskin leggings, decorated with intricate and colorful quill- and beadwork.

On the day before our departure, Lieutenant de Rouville sought me out, expressing his gratitude for my willingness to accompany the expedition. I assured him that, for the glory of God, I was prepared to share every hardship we might encounter, and to minister to the spiritual needs of our warriors and soldiers. Together, we repaired to the chapel to pray for the success of the mission, for we were to leave the next day.

Accordingly, in the pre-dawn gloom of the seventh day of February, the previous chaos having been miraculously transformed into order, we set forth on our journey of three hundred miles. Everyone was provided with snow shoes, without which it would have been impossible to proceed, the snow having reached a depth of at least three feet. The French officers, together with the Indian leaders, headed the cavalcade, followed by the warriors and *troupes de la marine*. Bringing up the rear was the commissariat of dog sleds laden with supplies. I strode alongside our Mohawks, rejoicing in the action. Oserohkoton came in search of me, expressing concern that my robe would become weighted with snow, and inviting me to join the pouches of parched corn, bark containers of dried moose meat and gourds of bear fat on the sleds. Laughing, I refused his good-natured offer. Then, to satisfy him, I pulled my *soutane* up to below my knees, secured it with my sash and, drawing his attention to my new leggings and snow shoes, showed him that I was able to keep up a steady pace with ease.

In the course of our journey, I continually marveled at the Indians' familiarity with the wilderness. What it provides, they use to their advantage. We crossed Lake Champlain over the ice. At night, we built shelters and beds of evergreens or slept in caves excavated in banks of snow. Indians are able to survive without hardship on a handful of parched corn a day, but for we French, hunger was a constant companion. On two occasions, Oserohkoton caught sight of deer in the depths of the forest. Silently alerting his comrades, he set off with long, lithe strides, his snow shoes carrying him effortlessly over the packed snow. The deer, hampered by the drifts, fell easy prey to his tomahawk and knife. When the Indians lit the customary fire on those nights, great was the comfort of hot broth and fresh meat.

I took advantage of one of these more relaxed occasions to ask Oserohkoton whether he had ever wanted to learn French, and acquire the skills of writing and reading. From one so intelligent and eager to learn in other respects, his answer surprised me.

"Some years ago, Father Chauchetière tried to teach our people your language," he said, "but it was not pleasing to our minds. Mohawk is the language God has given us. Through it, we speak to Him and to our ancestors. Through it we Kanien'keha:ka see the world as one people. We do not wish to lessen that oneness by eating from different dishes. Further, we have no need for writing, and therefore not for book reading either. We read what is before us on the bark of a tree where a bear has passed or a deer has licked. Our wampum preserves knowledge of important matters; our ceremonies honor the gifts of Nature and the passing of the seasons; our memories cherish what is needful for us to know as we go through life."

I inclined my head in respectful acknowledgment.

"The verities of your people are indeed different from those of ours. They accord with your way of being in the world. Living beside you, we have learned much that would otherwise have been unknown to us. In return, we have brought you knowledge of the Son of God."

"That is truly a great blessing, Father," he replied.

We had been traveling for twenty days, when de Rouville ordered that the sleds and dogs be left with a guard at a crossing on the Connecticut River to await our return. We were within twenty miles of our target—a day's march. De Rouville called a halt. Forbidding the lighting of the customary fire, he sent out scouts to observe the village. Reporting back before dawn, they said that there were no signs of militia, and that banks of snow piled against the stockade surrounding the settlement would aid in an assault. Calling the officers and the chiefs together, de Rouville gave them their orders. "Surprise is essential to the success of our enterprise. Make your way to the river with the utmost stealth, for doubtless there are scouts and watchmen. From the river it is a scant mile to the village. We will attack in the early hours of the morning." He then called on me to lead the men in prayer.

Getting under way long before dawn, by the pallid glow of a waning moon, we made good progress despite the difficult terrain, arriving at the river before sunset. The Indians made use of the remaining hour of light to apply their war paint and adjust the feather headdresses that distinguish one clan from another. Some had a ridge of hair down the middle of their shaved heads, a style used only when on the warpath. The scalps of most bore only a single lock.

We sat in total silence until four hours past midnight, when a scout returned to report that the watchman who had been pa-trolling the stockade was now nowhere to be seen. French officers, *troupes* and Christian Indians gathered around me. I lifted my voice in prayer. "Heavenly Father, we dedicate this mission to Thy greater glory. We submit ourselves to the protection of the Holy Virgin and give ourselves into Thy hands, knowing that whatever may befall us is according to Thy will. We ask Thy blessing on this enterprise and Thy guidance in our actions that they may bring us closer to Thy divine presence whether in this life or the next."

Leaving me, together with some of their number, on the far side of the river as a rear guard, and moving in ghostly silence, the assault force crossed the frozen river onto the meadow beyond, and melted into the blackness.

No sound, no sign—then, a glow on the horizon. The village was burning.

O, Étienne, the sight that greeted our eyes when the sun was about one hour risen! A trail of Indians leading or dragging men, women and children snaked across the meadow to where we were concealed. More than one hundred souls, distraught, weeping, bloodied, some clutching children to their bosoms, others looking frantically about and calling the names of husbands, wives, sons, daughters, all in terror of their lives. The last had barely reached us when we heard gunshots in the direction of the village. Far across the meadows, we saw a group of horsemen from neighboring settlements thundering to the rescue of their compatriots. In a wild chase, they put to flight those of our forces still making their way toward the river, killing or wounding many. Emboldened by their success, and unaware of our presence, the English continued their pursuit within range of our flintlocks. The officers called to order the reserve troops and those soldiers and Indians who had managed to rejoin us. Waiting until the assailants were almost upon us, our men fired, to great effect. A number of the enemy were killed or wounded; the remainder withdrew, turning and firing towards us until they were out of range.

When the tumult had died down, I looked about me. Many of the women captives had sunk upon the ground, some weeping, others staring as if in a nightmare. Near me, a distraught young mother tried to pacify her screaming infant. As I reached out to her in compassion, her Indian 'master' pushed me aside. Pulling the child from her arms, he killed it with one blow of his club. Incensed at the sight, a man—perhaps her husband— yelling in fury, wrenched free of his captor. A few steps, and he, too, lay lifeless in the snow.

Appalled that de Rouville was standing aloof, making no attempt to stop these barbarous murders, I confronted him. "Lieutenant," I said, "these unchristian killings of innocents cannot be allowed to continue."

"Father," he replied, "it is their custom. I cannot interfere. I would have a mutiny and probably a massacre on my hands. What is more, we French would lose our native allies. Their mission is to gain captives; ours is to depopulate the English frontier. In this way, we all win. Furthermore, you must realize that the Indians mainly do away with those they know will not survive the journey. To them, it is less cruel to kill children or faltering women quickly than to allow them to die slowly of privation."

Unwilling to provoke him, I did not speak what was in my

heart, for it seemed to me that sending savages, especially those who professed Christianity, to commit atrocities against the English was murder, and an unjust manner of waging war. Soberly I left him and went over to where some male captives were begging to be allowed to help their wives and children, pleas that were granted or denied according to the whims of their Indian masters. Prominent among them was an imposing man in clerical garb whom I assumed was Deerfield's minister. Wishing to pay my respects to a man of the cloth, albeit a heretic, I introduced myself in English and asked if I could be of service. Regarding me coldly, he drew himself up, saying that he would turn to a French soldier or even an Indian before making himself indebted to a minion of the pope. His Mohawk master, seeing me thus haughtily addressed, advanced on him with his club raised. I stayed his hand, saying, "It is of no account. He speaks out of ignorance of the one true faith. God willing, he may in time come to see the error of his beliefs." With that, I went on my way, with heaviness in my heart. I later learned that the minister's name was John Williams, captured with his wife and five of their children, the two youngest having been clubbed before his eyes in the attack on the village. As a man of standing among the English, he was obviously a valuable prize, and therefore potentially a useful hostage.

Shortly after this encounter, de Rouville ordered that all should start marching in single file and gather at the foot of a hill about a mile away. Stragglers were still arriving, among the last being a number of Indians and French carrying their wounded. I hastened to meet them, so that I could administer the *viaticum* to any who might be near death. To my distress, I found Oserohkoton among the casualties. Supported by a comrade, he was making his way with difficulty to the river, a blood stain spreading on the right-hand side of his deerskin tunic. A bullet had pierced the upper part of his chest, but had not exited, and I feared that it had lodged in a bone, increasing the danger of infection. Unable to administer any immediate medical aid, I indicated to his comrade that I would thenceforth accompany him, and we joined the trail of ragged humanity making its labored way through the snow.

When all had gathered at the rendezvous, the captives were made to surrender their shoes, in place of which their captors gave them moccasins. Without them it is certain that few would have survived the journey. I busied myself with tending the wounded, of whom eight were Indians, and close to twenty officers and *troupes*. Lacking Paré's recommended rosewater and egg yolk to combine with my supply of turpentine, I perforce used only the latter to cleanse torn flesh, staunching the flow of blood with ligatures and lint padding. I was encouraged to find that Oserohkoton's wound did not appear to have injured his lung, and, knowing the extraordinary power of his body and spirit, I prayed that with God's help and my ministrations he would recover.

While I was thus engaged, some of the Indians set about fashioning basket slings consisting of elm or hickory frames, fitted with seats of hide thongs, in which to transport their wounded. Our countrymen, unwilling to emulate the 'savages,' constructed litters which proved to be useless on the narrow trails and in the icy conditions we encountered, and they were forced, after two days, to carry their comrades on their backs.

At last, the preparations having been completed, the injured warriors were squeezed into the sturdy contrivances and firmly secured with their knees under their chins. The discomfort and pain caused by these constrictions must have been considerable, but the Indians showed no signs of distress. They were then hoisted onto their comrades' backs and suspended by straps around the foreheads or chests of their 'steeds.' I offered to carry Oserohkoton or one of the other wounded, but the Indians courteously refused, saying it was a duty that warriors assumed for their fellows. Several of the casualties, both Indian and French, died in the following days, and were buried in the snow.

Packs of supplies having been distributed among the Indians and *troupes*, or loaded onto the backs of some of the captive men, we prepared to march in earnest. An unseasonable thaw accompanied by rain exacerbated the miseries of our first day's march, our sorry band progressing barely five miles. On the following day, several women, some weak from recent child-bearing and lacking snowshoes, were floundering and falling in the half-melted snow. Among them was Reverend Williams's wife. For a short time, he was permitted by his captor to help her, but eventually was forced to leave her behind. Throughout the morning, he asked other captives if they had seen her. At last, one had news. Having slipped and fallen in an icy stream and being unable to rise, her captor had slain her with a hatchet. Turning aside, his shoulders heaving, the minister gave way to his grief. Impulsively, I reached out to him, but refrained from touching him, for I knew that my comfort would have been as brimstone to him.

Several other women, unable to keep up, were similarly dispatched by their masters. Among the men, one who refused to accept the authority of his captor was immediately tomahawked. The younger children, being more likely to adapt to Indian ways, were precious as potential new tribal members. Wrapped in fur robes their masters carried them and treated them with kindness. That night, and throughout our march, our captors tied the more valuable captives to the ground. One man, not thus tethered, escaped. When this was discovered the next day, de Rouville commanded Reverend Williams to warn the captives that if any more tried to escape, the Indians would burn the rest alive.

On the third day, having covered in my judgment perhaps fifteen miles, the Indians stopped to tally the number of captives remaining, debating among themselves regarding their distribution. Some warriors had more than one and others none, and it is their custom that all should share equally. It was here, too, that the Indians plundered the captives of anything of value, even clothing, which they then sold to the soldiers, who in turn gave their dirty castoffs to the English.

These matters at last having been resolved to the Indians' satisfaction, we resumed our painful progress, in which pangs of hunger and cold exacerbated those of grief and shock. To the town dwellers, the wilderness was a place of manifold dangers, every owl's screech or paw print adding to their terrors. There was no relief from the aching chill, no comfort in the handful of groundnuts and shavings of dried moose meat that was their portion at night, no escape from the ghastly images that haunted their dreams. When bitter winds howled and chilled me to the core, it seemed my bones would crack like the brittle boughs about me. At times, to relieve an Indian who had been carrying a child for hours, I would take his burden, finding comfort in the human connection and the warmth. I would also try to ease the way of the struggling women, both young and old, helping them through the broken ice of streams and over fallen trees, or supporting them on frozen paths. Some could not overcome their abhorrence of priests and would not allow me to approach them. The sufferings of others were greater than their prejudices, and they tolerated my aid.

And yet, Étienne, amid these tribulations there were times when it seemed that I stood apart, observing myself and my fellow travelers with a deep and objective compassion. At such times, I would make my way at night into the woods where the snow's purity and the blessed silence brought peace to my soul and strength to my spirit. Such is the love of God, Who brings sustenance to those who seek it.

Three agonizing days followed the same pattern, with threats and killings depressing the spirits of captives already numbed by the tragedies they had witnessed and the deprivations undermining their bodily strength. At last we reached the Connecticut River where we had left the dogs, the sleds and the bulk of our supplies, including twenty moose, which had been carefully cached. The wounded, suffering from endless jolting, buffeting by snow-laden branches, and occasional immersions in icy streams, were now afforded deliverance from their ordeal, being loaded onto the sleds, along with some of the provender, to be transported on the frozen river. Most of the party, however, continued on foot along its banks.

So far, there had been no signs of pursuit, the English doubtless being aware that their compatriots would be slain if any attempt to rescue them were made. Consequently, the Indians relaxed their severity, though not their vigilance. When de Rouville called a day of rest, the Indians built a large fire on which they cooked a stew of moose and groundnuts in iron pots, sharing it out among captors and captives alike. To the great comfort of his flock, Rev. Williams was permitted to preach a sermon. He chose a text from the Book of Lamentations: "The Lord is righteous, for I have rebelled against his commandment. Hear I pray you, all people, and behold my sorrow. My virgins and my young men have gone into captivity."

The following day, somewhat refreshed in body and spirit, we prepared to continue our march. I was relieved to see that our unwieldy company was to split up, for from this point we would have to live off the land. The French force, depleted in number from its losses at Deerfield, set off for Québec. Our Mohawks and some Abenakis chose to follow the White River through the Green Mountains.

It is difficult, dear brother, to describe the torments we endured. Despite my daily ministrations, Oserohkoton's wound had become infected. He had developed a fever, and although he begged to be left to die, the Mohawk were deaf to his pleas. Day after endless day, on bruised, frozen and swollen feet, the rats of hunger gnawing ceaselessly at our vitals and our strength, we struggled along the icy banks of streams or stumbled on rough, slippery trails. In the third week of our Calvary, after a day's grueling march, we at last reached Lake Champlain. Relieved to find that the ice was still firm, the Indians became more relaxed and, having crossed the lake, made a detour to a village where we broke our long fast on moose, fish, cranberries and, most delightfully, goose. There we tarried several days, during which time I was able to pay particular attention to Oserohkoton. His wound was now suppurating severely, and his eyes were glassy with fever. I believe that he had only survived this far because of his devout wish to be buried in Christian ground among his ancestors. Recognizing the need to hasten Oserohkoton's return to Kahnawake, I and two of his clansmen determined to set forth ahead of the main party. It being early April, the rivers were running free enough to be navigable. Oserohkoton's companions therefore spent a day building an elm-bark canoe, which brought us to Fort Chambly in two days, almost a month after leaving Deerfield. The following evening we arrived at Kahnawake, where we were received with rejoicing at our preservation, and with lamentation at the realization that the breath of life was leaving Oserohkoton. Ontasaga drew the sled bearing his dying son to Onatah's longhouse, and laid him with infinite care on a bear skin near the entrance. There, I administered the *viaticum* and extreme unction, and prayed beside him in company with his family until his soul departed in the early hours of the second day. His clan brothers surrounded his bier. Heads bowed, they remained there in total silence from dawn until the sun reached its zenith.

Thus passed from the earth a noble soul, leaving me to mourn the loss of a brother spirit. In the twilight of that sad day, I sat with Ontasaga and Onatah as laments for their beloved son arose from the depths of their grieving hearts.

My son, my son,

keeper of the wellspring of our aged ones,

you have gone to comfort them with youth and strength.

Too soon you have gone, too soon.

You, who were brother to the eagle,

who walked in the ways of the Great Spirit,

whose song of life gladdened all Creation.

In this beaver robe we enfold you,

in a robe of the spirit of the waters we lay you to rest

that you may come at last to a place of peace.

℘

His soul has fled.

O Ontasaga, my husband, it has fled

to where we may not follow.

He has gone where we may never take him by the hand—

that small boy, that bright spirit, who was a gift from God,

and taught us what love is.

His breath is no more, my husband,

and all he might have been, here among us,

now will never be.

He will be of the company of Jesus,

in the presence of God, Whose ways are beyond understanding.

May He take pity on the darkness in my heart.

May He send me one for whom my love

will be like rain upon parched land;

one who will be worthy of my lost son.

❦

Some weeks have passed since the death of Oserohkoton, and it is only now that I have the heart to continue this letter.

The main party of our expedition reached Chambly ten days after our arrival at the fort. We learned that, through God's mercy, ninety-two of the one hundred and twelve unfortunates taken at Deerfield had survived their ordeal, sixteen women and children and four men having died or been killed along the way.

The longer I stay in the New World, Étienne, the more my mind ponders the mysteries of humankind. Daily I witness the Indians' love of children, yet how to reconcile that with their slaying of innocents on our long journey from Deerfield? I have witnessed, too, many instances of their loyalty and kindness to each other, their fierce pride in keeping their word, their courage and self-control in the worst of circumstances, even to the point, I have been told, of never flinching under torture. There lies the riddle, for among these otherwise admirable people, the torture of war captives is routine, though less frequent now, thanks to the influence of our brothers in Christ. Captive men, whether Indian or European, are often humiliated by having the forefinger of their right hand chopped off as a sign of servitude and to prevent them from firing a bow or a gun. Some are burned alive in revenge for causing the death of a kinsman. Yet, unlike in Europe, the violation of captured women is seldom, if ever, practiced. We accuse the Natives of barbarism, yet what was the burning of heretics in the recent past if not savagery? Is scalping more perfidious than exhibiting severed heads on city walls? And what in the demonic arsenal of torturers is more abominable than the rack? The intensity of my experiences in this strange land arouses many questions and sometimes doubts. I pray daily to discern whether it is God's will that in the course of our quest to bring souls into the light of our religion, we Jesuits align ourselves with forces that cause an infinity of those living in darkness to perish before being saved. In patience I await His answer.

Discussion of such weighty questions must be left to a later time. For now, let us rejoice in the news, just lately received here, of the great storm that chastised our enemy last November. It is a sign of God's favor to our cause that He released His fury on the English fleet. The report we received recounted that the winds raged for more than a week, destroying thirteen ships with great loss of life, and ravaging coastal cities. May this be a sign that France will emerge victorious from the conflict convulsing her domains. *Soli Deo honor et Gloria.*

I trust that this lengthy chronicle will be of interest to you. I leave it to your discretion as to whether you impart its contents to our mother, some of which may be troubling to her gentle soul. To have you as my secular "confessor" is a comfort indeed. May God bless you and keep you.

Yours in Christ,

Vincent S.J.

Chauncy, Massachusetts
August 8 1704

What does the future hold for a seven-year-old boy who awakes in a New England attic on a steamy August morning in 1704? Is it to become a farmer like his father? Is he to be among the fortunate few to attend a dame school? He has unusual quickness of mind. Perhaps the life of a soldier or merchant—maybe even that of a lawyer or minister—lies ahead. Such are the dreams of his mother. They do not enter the consciousness of Timothy Rice but her voice through the open trapdoor rouses him. "Boys, it is time to rise," he hears through the fog of sleep, and, reluctant to start the day so early, buries his face in the straw mattress he shares with his brothers. Not until nine-year-old Silas shakes his arm does he wake sufficiently to stumble to the ladder and call down to her, "Mother, is Nahor to come with us?" "Your father wishes you and Silas to teach him," comes the reply. "Make haste, for you are to leave after breakfast."

He leans over the small boy still curled in sleep. "Wake up, Nahor," he says, shaking the five-year-old's plump shoulder. "You're to come with Silas and me to the flax field. You are a big boy now."

No need to dress, for he has slept in his clothes. He scrambles down the ladder. Holding baby Moses on her hip, Ruth Rice is ladling corn mush into bowls, drizzles it with molasses. His mouth waters and his stomach aches as he sweeps the hearthstone clear of ash. He had misspoken parts of his catechism the night before, and his father had sent him to bed without supper. To take his mind off his hunger, he reads Dinah's sampler that hangs behind his father's chair, lips moving as he silently spells out the longer words: "A holy family is a place of comfort, a church of God."

His father, Edmund, comes in from the stable with Silas, both carrying heavy pails of milk. When the father and sons are seated, the mother and eleven-year-old Dinah place bowls before them. All bow their heads. "O Lord our God," says Edmund Rice, "Blessed be thy holy name, for these thy good benefits, wherewith thou hast so plentifully at this time refreshed our bodies. O Lord vouchsafe ..."

"What does that word mean?" Timothy wonders. He ventures a furtive glance around the table. Out of the corner of his eye he sees his little sister strapped into her wooden chair, babbling in three-year-old language to her corn-husk doll. "Wish I could stay and mind Huldah instead of working in the hot sun," he thinks, then quickly closes his eyes.

" ... unto life everlasting," his father is saying. "Forgive us our sins, and grant us health, peace, and truth, in Jesus Christ, our Lord and only Savior. Amen."

After the echoed "Amen," the bowls are emptied in silence.

Timothy becomes conscious of his father's stern gaze as they walk towards the door. "There will be no faltering over your catechism this evening, Timothy, or it will be the switch for you."

Dismay as he thinks of the hard day's work before him. When will he have time to go over the catechism? "But father ..." he begins.

"No buts! Willfulness will be your undoing, my boy. Find a way to learn what you must."

"Yes, father."

Shoulders slumped, Timothy joins his brothers outside.

"You can repeat the catechism to me while we walk," whispers Silas. "I know it well."

Ruth hands her husband a basket.

"Here is your dinner," she says. "Do not be too harsh on Timothy, Husband. He is making excellent progress with the primer and has almost overtaken Silas."

"The more reason to teach him humility," says Edmund, and turns to go.

"Please make sure the boys wear their hats," says Ruth. "I shall look for you before nightfall."

She stands beside the house on Powder Hill. Behind her, Lake Naggawoomcom gleams silver in the early light. She is grateful to remain at home, with Dinah to help with candle-making, harvesting beans and minding the young ones. She watches her husband and sons walk down the sloping path until they reach the woods. Before they enter its shade, Timothy turns to wave. Moses, in his mother's arms, and Huldah, clinging to her skirt, flutter their small hands.

In less than a mile, father and sons reach a house where their neighbor, David Maynard, is waiting to join them. The sun is now visible above the horizon.

"Give you good morrow, neighbor," he says. "It bids fair to be a fine day for the harvest." The men talk about farming and the affairs of their small settlement. Timothy remembers the flax field earlier that year, bluer than the summer sky. In the mysterious, cool green below the eye-high flowers, he and his brothers and cousins had stalked each other.

"Do you think we can play at Indians today, Silas? Like last time?"

"Perhaps, when we have finished our tasks."

Another mile, and they reach the fields, which lie close by his Uncle Thomas's garrison house. Now, the flax stalks are turning yellow, their brown seed pods rustling in the slight breeze. Queen Anne's Lace and chicory, Blackeyed Susans and white daisies nod among them. Some neighbors are already hard at work, for the flax harvest is a communal task. Edmund's sons find their cousins, Ashur and Adonijah, helping to lay the pulled stems out to dry.

The boys greet each other joyfully. "Mind now, no playing until your work is complete," admonishes Edmund. "Silas, make sure your brothers wear their hats or they will fall ill with sun-sickness." He goes off to join the men and women pulling up the flax plants, and the boys are left alone.

BLENHEIM, GERMANY

AUGUST 13, 1704

In southern Bavaria, along the River Nebel, the French army is deployed—fifty-six thousand cavalrymen and infantry with their horses, cannons, muskets, bayonets and supply wagons, their trumpets, drums and drapeaux d'ordonnance. *For sixty years, this juggernaut has been undefeated, and Marshal Tallard and his generals are justly proud of the many victories achieved in the name of their commander-in-chief, Louis XIV, the Sun King, who dreams of drawing all of Europe into his glittering orbit.*

On this day, a four-mile phalanx of white tents links the villages of Lutzinger and Oberglauheim to their sister village of Blenheim, perched beside the Danube that winds its timeless way from the Black Forest to the Black Sea. Before them, a peaceful vista of marshes, meadows and stubbled fields; behind and beyond, dark forests of guardian pines.

In one of the tents, relieved at last from his daily duties as a cavalry officer in the Touraine regiment, Étienne de Surville pauses, quill in hand, to gaze across the narrow, marshy Nebel at the grass rippling in the evening breeze. Before him, on a chest that serves as a table, a short letter awaits his signature. It is dated the twelfth of August in the year 1704 and is addressed to La Comtesse Aurélie de Surville, in care of the sisters of Fontevraud Abbey, Touraine, France.

My dear mother, it begins, after many weeks of marching, we have at last established an encampment. Thus far, we have not engaged the enemy. Indeed, the best efforts of our scouts have failed to detect the presence of the British and their allies in this area. As you know, I am not permitted to reveal anything concerning our location or actions, but I wished to take advantage of this peaceful time to assure you of my good health, and my devotion.

In the waning light, he dips his quill and signs: Your ever-dutiful son, Étienne.

He wakes to sounds of signal guns and confusion, pushes aside the tent flaps. *Great Providence!* Like Spartoi sprung from dragon's teeth on the fields of Kolkhis, legions of armed warriors stand where grasses waved. He reaches for his uniform, is belted and buckled by the time his groom appears, his chestnut charger accoutered for battle. Carbine, pistol, sword in their assigned places, he mounts and rides to join his regiment.

The enemy opens fire. Over several hours, cannons and muskets, swords and bayonets take their terrible toll. Amid the smell of gunpowder and smoke and blood, rising above the human shrieks, the horses' terrified whinnying, the thin sound of a trumpet orders the French cavalry to the relief of Blenheim. *Mon Dieu!* Our elite Gens d'Armes are fleeing! Thousands of our soldiers are trapped within the village. They are packed so densely they cannot defend themselves for fear of killing their comrades.

The relief force temporarily repulses the enemy. Back and forth through the long afternoon, shooting, slashing, slaying wherever its strength is needed. Benumbed, outnumbered, Étienne's wearied contingent cannot withstand the onslaught of the Prussian Life Dragoons. Driven en masse *toward the Danube, thousands drown. Before they reach the river, some few on the flank are carried by force of numbers over the edge of a shallow ravine. Étienne is among them. A shooting pain as his horse falls on him. Then, oblivion.

☙ ❧

At the sound of a voice, his mind swims to consciousness. "Celui-ci est encore vivant," (this one is still alive) it is saying. The crack of a shot, and the weight pinning him to the ground stops moving. His horse is dead. When next he opens his eyes, he is in a canvas shelter. Groans and screams whirl about him. Some are louder than the others. He realizes they are issuing from his own mouth. Someone gives him water, brandy. A piece of wood between his teeth. Then, pain beyond all bearing.

He wakes on a rough cot. He struggles to rise. A strong arm pushes him down. "Imbecile! You think you can walk on one leg?" His left arm is rigid. It is in a splint. He sinks again to a place where pain cannot reach.

LETTER FOUR

New France

(four months later)

Kahnawake, New France, the 3ʳᵈ Day of October, 1704

Dear Étienne,

It is some months since I received a letter from you, and my fervent hope is that nothing of grave import has occurred to prevent your writing.

How strange it is to contemplate that when I wake and prepare for Matins, your day is already advanced to the hour of noon! One evening last winter I calculated that the sun rises six hours earlier for you than it does for us here in the New World. Time is indeed one of God's mysteries, for despite its passage your face, and that of our mother, remain as fresh to me as when I last saw you. I think often of her work among the poor of our village, which was an example to us all, and remarkable because she did not allow our father's disapproval to turn her from what she saw as her Christian duty.

Here at Kahnawake, we have been receiving regular reports on the fates of the captives taken at Deerfield. First, the Williams family. Soon after arriving in Montreal, Reverend Williams and his daughter, Esther, were redeemed by Governor Philippe de Rigaud Vaudreuil. It is possible that the minister will be exchanged for Pierre Maisonnat de Baptiste, a French privateer held by the English, in which case Reverend Williams will return to Deerfield. A French merchant redeemed fifteen-year-old Samuel Williams and sent him to a school where, to his father's dismay, he is receiving instruction in our faith. Stephen, aged nine, and Eunice, aged seven, sojourned several months in Indian villages with their captors before coming to Kahnawake. The boy has rejoined his father, but, despite the governor's adjurations, the Mohawks refuse to relinquish Eunice, who is precious to them. The youngest boy, Warham, was ransomed by a French gentlewoman. Several Deerfield men have been cruelly enslaved by their Indian masters. Some women were placed in convents, their redeemers being anxious for their conversion to our faith; others, men and women, were sold to the French as indentured servants. The rest of the captives have been adopted into their captors' communities. It is deplorable that some of our Indians, as well as certain unscrupulous French merchants, now see captive-taking as a lucrative form of trade. This situation is of great concern to Governor Dudley of Massachusetts, who has been negotiating with Governor Vaudreuil to institute a system of prisoner exchange that would eliminate ransom.

However regrettable this captive-taking may be, it is nevertheless a matter of satisfaction to me and my *confrères* that many of the unbelievers brought to New France are receiving instruction in our Catholic faith from our brother missionaries, the French *habitants* and the Christian Indians. It is a difficult task to turn them from their heresies, for the Protestants cling to their catechism and mistaken beliefs with blind obduracy, professing a horror of 'popish superstition.' They have an antipathy to crossing themselves or kneeling to pray, and stop their ears at the sound of Latin prayers. Some will not even enter our church. Yet others have come to accept the grace of baptism and instruction in our holy faith, for which we daily offer thanks.

But enough of such musing, for I wish to recount a remarkable occurrence. Some days ago, upon hearing that a further party of captives was approaching, I went to stand on a small rise which allowed me to see beyond the palisade where a crowd was gathering. Indians take delight in the custom of the gauntlet—now thankfully rarer than in the past—inflicted on male captives. Forming two long rows between which the victims must pass, men, women and children rain blows on naked prisoners, belaboring them not only with clubs and sticks, but with jeers and taunts. Indians have contempt for mental and physical weakness; thus, any captive who falls and is unable to rise, is summarily killed.

Some distance from the gate, two Mohawks stood, each restraining a young captive boy by the shoulders. As the first gauntlet victim completed his ordeal and staggered into the compound, a second was prodded toward the *bastinado*. Reeling and stumbling under the onslaught, he fell. When his tormentors saw he could not get up, they dispatched him with a club. An emaciated man was next. As he passed the boys, one of them reached out to him, but was pulled back by his captor. Crouching and staggering, the man was receiving blow upon blow when the boy wrenched himself free. Ducking below the flailing clubs and grasping the man's hand, he stood erect, receiving several severe blows before the Indians realized he was there. To my amazement, the wild whooping stopped. Raising their clubs as if in salute, the Indians allowed the man to stumble through the long walk of his reprieve led by a child.

Bemused, I glanced around to find my *confrères* had joined me on the vantage point. Meeting my questioning gaze, Father Lamberville remarked, "The boy has courage. He did not know that the Mohawk seldom subject children to that trial."

In the hiatus, the boy's captor strode forward. Passing between the lines, he reached the boy and hoisted him onto his shoulder. It was then that I recognized the man as Ontasaga.

"Behold my son!" he cried to the onlookers. "He will take the honored place of Oserohkoton. He will be of our clan and our family."

Striding the length of the gauntlet, he presented the boy to the clan mothers, who were gathered to indicate their acceptance or rejection of each captive. The women received the boy with smiles and gestures of approval, whereupon Ontasaga's wife, Onatah, came forward. "My tears are dried," she declared loudly, so that all could hear. Then, taking the boy by the hand, she led him toward the village. Twisting in her grasp, he looked over his shoulder in an attempt to ascertain the fate of the man he had rescued. Perhaps to honor the child's courage, the women did not demand that the pitiful prisoner be killed. Instead, he was claimed by his scowling captor and pushed roughly along the path to the village, in all likelihood to endure a life of slavery.

The pandemonium resumed, and, distressed by the violence, I turned away, musing on the spectacle I had just witnessed. I wanted to see more of this child who, though bruised and confused, had risen with such dignity above the crowd. I wanted to know his story. Above all, I wanted to save him from the Puritan heresies that were doubtless his patrimony, for I sensed that, once girded and guided by the truths of our faith, he was destined for greatness.

Returning later to my quarters, I opened the Iroquois Book of Rites compiled by my predecessors in the Way of the Lord. I found the passage that had caught my attention:

> "Great thanks now, therefore, that you have safely arrived. Now, then, let us smoke the pipe together. Because all around are hostile agencies which are each thinking, "I will frustrate their purpose." Here thorny ways, and here falling trees, and here wild beasts lying in ambush. Either by these you might have perished, my offspring, or, here by floods you might have been destroyed, my offspring, or by the uplifted hatchet in the dark outside the house. Every day these are wasting us; or deadly invisible disease might have destroyed you, my offspring."

The boy had confronted perils on his long journey through the wilderness. My task will be to help him recognize the perils of his misdirected faith.

 C3 80

Hunched on the sleeping shelf where he has spent a sleepless night, Timothy's mind gropes for a center.

Is this now to be his home? This vast, smoke-filled cavern smelling of skins and fish and bear grease, shared with ten families and mice and fleas? How can he ever think of this dark woman as his mother, which she insists she is. She has kind eyes, but . . . his mother! Never! His real mother, the one who bore him . . . so gentle, so loving. He longs to comfort

*her, to explain why he and his brothers did not come home, why Nahor
... his father couldn't save Nahor. And he didn't even try to rescue him
and Silas. And now Ashur and Adonijah are gone and he may never see
them again. And what if the Indians attack the house on Powder Hill?
Will his father be able to protect his mother and sisters and little Moses?
Huldah and Moses—do they miss him? Do his mother and Dinah?*

*He likes Ontasaga. He was scared of him at first, but afterwards he
taught him how to find ground-nuts and shoot with a bow and arrow
and build an elm-bark canoe. Thanks to Ontasaga, he and Silas could
survive in the woods ... perhaps they could escape and return home. He
is sure they could follow the trail back--they both took note of hills and
streams, rocks and groups of trees on the way to Kahnawake. But ... if
he went home he would never learn to hunt like the Indians or paddle
a canoe through the rapids. And every Sunday he would have to walk
hours to church and listen for hours to two sermons. Now, when he dies
he will go to hell because he is forgetting his catechism. Silas won't help
him. He says if they're never going back there's no need to remember it.
Anyway, perhaps they'll be forced to become Catholics, which would be
worse than becoming like Indians. He didn't know why, but that's what
their father had said.*

*He senses someone near him. Then a voice ... a voice speaking Eng-
lish words ...*

C3 80

The following day I made my way to Onatah's longhouse. In
the smoky gloom, lit only by a shaft of sunlight entering through a
smoke hole, I saw Onatah seated by her fire pit. Having greeted her
in Mohawk, I looked around for the boy. On the sleeping platform
opposite her, I discerned his small figure. Gone was the vibrant
energy of the day before. He sat, head bent, thin arms clasping
knees to chin. I requested Onatah's permission to address him, then
asked in English, "What is your name, my son?" At the sound of his
native tongue, the motionless child's muscles tensed and he raised
his head. On seeing my cassock, his eyes registered alarm before he
resumed his former pose. "I am Father Vincent," I said. "Any time
you would like to talk, I will listen." Thanking Onatah, I departed.

In the course of performing my duties in the village over the next few days, I was interested to see the boy joining in some games with his peers, but he did not attempt to approach me. Then, late one afternoon, while I was writing in our common room, there came a knock at the door. I opened it to find the boy standing there. Keeping his face averted, he said, "I have a question."

"Let us see if I can answer it."

"Why does Onatah say she is my mother? She is *not* my mother. She says I must not speak to my brother Silas in English, and she cannot teach me my letters because she does not know what writing is. She tries to teach me counting with corn stalks, but I already know my numbers and how to add them together. I like some of the things she cooks, but I *hate* bear grease." Looking up with moist eyes, he said, "And now my real mother has only my sisters and baby brother at home."

"Onatah is a good and wise woman. She has many things to teach you, and she, too, has lost a son. Will you tell me your name so that we may talk more easily?"

"Timothy Rice" he said.

"How old are you, Timothy?"

"What month is it now?"

"It is October."

"I was born on the fifteenth day of September, so I must be eight, because I was seven when Ontasaga took me from my family."

At that moment, the bell rang for Vespers. I rose from my chair.

"I am pleased to know you, Timothy Rice," I said. "I am needed now at the church, but I would like to hear more of your story when you are ready to tell it."

Head bowed, he turned his back on me. Scuffing his feet in the dusty pathway he made his way to the village.

Wishing to ascertain Onatah's experience with Timothy, I sought her out the following day. I referred to my encounter with him and remarked that it seemed he was having difficulty adjusting to his new surroundings.

"His spirit suffers," she said. "It is natural. His roots have not yet found nourishment in this strange soil and his brother is his sole comfort. His past and his whiteness must be washed away soon so that he may find peace. At the new moon, he will be adopted into the Turtle Clan. It will help him to feel that we are his family."

With his adoption only a month away, I had limited opportunity for getting to know Timothy as an English boy and a Puritan before he became a Mohawk (how grateful I am to have learned his language at the seminary!), which I felt was important in determining my interactions with him. I accordingly arranged for Ontasaga to bring him to me daily until the ceremony.

At the first of these regular meetings he would not meet my gaze. Was I not the embodiment of all that he had been taught to fear even more than the Indians, and indeed more than death itself? I invited him to sit on a bench opposite me and, seeking to set him at ease, asked whether Silas was in good health and if he was content with his new life.

"Silas likes being here better than I do," he said.

"Why do you think that is?"

"He is two years older than I am, and our father used to make him work hard. He had to help with our cow and our pig and carry heavy pails of water and work in the fields. I mostly helped my mother in the kitchen and the vegetable garden, and often Nahor and I (his voice broke) minded our baby sister. Sometimes our father would whip Silas if he made a mistake in reciting his catechism. And if we could not relate the Scripture stories properly, he told us we were sinful and would go to Hell. It made us so afraid we could not sleep at night." Raising his head to look at me for the first time, he asked, "Do you believe in Hell?"

"I believe that a soul that is filled with the love of God has no reason to fear Lucifer, who reigns over the hell of the sinful."

"I will tell Silas what you have said."

Pensively, he rose and moved towards the door, then slowly turned to face me.

"One winter, my father made me a toy wagon…"

Slowly, day by day, when he saw that I did not subject him to 'the darkness of Popish superstition,' he began to talk, cautiously at first, then eagerly, as if relieving himself of a burden too heavy for his eight years. I have tried to put together a coherent whole from his bursts of facts and imaginings in the hope that his experiences, which are similar in many respects to those of other captives, will be of interest to you, and of value to people who wish to be informed about these times.

It seems that in early August of this year, in the hamlet of Chauncy, Massachusetts, Timothy, his older brother, Silas, and his younger brother, Nahor, went with their father, Edmund Rice, to harvest flax in the fields adjacent to the garrison house of Edmund's brother, Thomas.

"It was hard work and it was very hot, but I was happy because when we were finished working, I could play with Ashur and Adonijah." Timothy told me. "They are my cousins."

As the adults pulled up the plants, the children laid them along the banks of a stream. Timothy was helping five-year-old Nahor to spread the stalks, when demonic whooping rent the air. Suddenly, Nahor was no longer there. Timothy froze, then raised his eyes. A mask-like face, streaked with red and black, hung over him. Before he could cry out, he was snatched by the wrists and flung onto a man's back. He could hear Nahor somewhere ahead screaming in terror. As his captor ran, with Timothy hanging like a sack, the shrieks became louder because Nahor's captor had stopped. At the moment that Timothy passed, the Indian raised his tomahawk and killed Nahor with one blow. Fists clenched and face deathly white, the boy shook uncontrollably as he told me this.

Timothy saw that Silas, Ashur and Adonijah had also been captured. To relieve his aching arms, he struggled in vain to wrap his legs around the Mohawk's body, which was slippery with bear grease. In the heat, the strange odor became overpowering, and he was close to fainting. At last, when the sun had passed noon, their captors dropped the boys to the ground. With threatening signs and rough prodding, they were made to understand that they would no longer be carried, but, seeing that their terror-weakened legs refused to move, the Indians dragged them along. By sundown, the boys were close to collapse.

When darkness was far advanced, the Indians stopped in a small clearing.

"There were eight of them," Timothy continued. "We were afraid of wolves and bears, but they did not light a fire for fear of being discovered," he said, adding bitterly, "My father did not come. I prayed that he would find us, but God did not hear me. He never came." I explained that if his father had come in pursuit, the Indians would have killed their captives. He was not to be mollified. "He should have come," he said.

The rest of his account was a confusion of images and half-remembered emotions. For many nights, until danger of pursuit was passed, he was made to lie between two Indians, in terror of moving in case they should club him, thinking he was trying to escape. When he closed his eyes in fitful sleep, an owl's hoot became the whooping that tore him from his family, the fall of a bough the blow that killed Nahor. He recalled that one of the band removed thorns from Silas's feet, and dressed Adonijah's cut toe with oak leaves bound with sinew. The boys' perpetual hunger was barely eased with meager meals of berries, groundnuts and parched corn. One event he recalled vividly. After walking for many days, they heard distant hollering and whooping. Reaching the top of a hill, they saw smoke rising from a number of wigwams in the valley below. As they approached the settlement, Timothy was amazed to see white people amid the smoke. It seemed to him that he was about to enter hell itself, for children's wails and women's weeping mingled with the ululating of Indians brandishing clubs and tomahawks.

"I feared that they were going to kill us," he said, "but Ashur thought maybe they would just sell us, for his father told him the Indians often sold captives to the French." With a sideways glance at me, he added, "We were in great fear that would happen to us, because they would have made us become Catholics."

"Would that be so terrible, my son?" I asked.

"My father said it would be worse than if we became savages," he replied.

It appears that they had arrived at a place where not only tribal groups, but also French and Dutch agents, gathered to trade captives for rum, guns, cooking pots, knives and other metal goods, or beaver pelts. At this point in the story, Timothy covered his face with his hands.

"Adonijah's master traded him to a French man for a knife," he murmured. "Just a knife..." After several minutes, he raised his head and said, "A Dutch man tried to buy me for two fowling pieces, but Ontasaga refused, so he bought Ashur instead for a cask of rum." With infinite sadness he added, "My cousins were so scared, and Silas and I did not even have a chance to bid them farewell."

It was at this trading camp that Timothy had befriended Elijah Briggs, the man he rescued from the gauntlet.

"When we left the camp, Mr. Briggs's band traveled with us," said Timothy. "They were Abenakis, and they say the English stole their land so they hate them. I saw that his master treated Mr. Briggs very badly. He beat him and starved him, so I gave him some of my food when I could. His master would have killed me if he had found out."

Once there was no longer danger of pursuit, the Indians ceased pushing the boys almost beyond their strength and treated them with kindness. Ontasaga and his clansman, who was Silas's master, knew a few words of English, and as their journey of more than a month progressed through the hills of Vermont to the shores of Lake Champlain, they started teaching the boys the lore of the woods, and giving them small tasks.

"Silas and I know how to shoot with a bow and arrow," Timothy told me, standing tall and pushing out his chest, "and how to choose an elm tree to make a canoe, and how to harvest groundnuts. Ontasaga taught us on the way to Kahnawake."

I tried conversing with Timothy in the Mohawk tongue, and was amazed at how many words and concepts he had mastered in so short and at so dire a time. And yet I should not have been amazed. Language is a reflection of our surroundings and experiences, and I have seen the power that wilderness exerts on humans. The Indians understand and use this power for their survival, finding meaning in every broken twig, paw print, or ripple on a pool, and even the direction of the wind. Many of the children brought into Indian society embrace its ways. I believe Timothy will be one of them; but preparing him to receive the sacraments of confession and communion—that, Étienne, is another matter entirely.

I anxiously await news of the war in Europe and of your part in it. Here in the New World we suffer for the sins of the Old. May there soon be an end to this madness, and may you come through it unharmed.

I trust that our mother remains in good health, and that your duties allow you to see her from time to time. Please convey my devotions to her. You are both ever in my prayers. God bless you.

Yours in Christ,
Vincent, S.J.

Chauncy, Massachusetts

The shadows lengthen on Powder Hill. Within the house, Moses sleeps in his cradle beside the hearth, while his mother sings a lullaby to Huldah lying on the trundle bed she shares with Dinah. When the child's eyes close, Ruth rises and moves to the open door.

"Dinah!" she calls softly as the girl approaches with the last of the beans in a basket. "See if your father and the boys are coming up the hill. I expected them ere this."

The shadows lengthen on Powder Hill. Do you see them yet, Dinah? I see nothing, Mother. Only the moon rising. What has delayed them? I see two figures, Mother. They are carrying guns.

Are the boys not with them, Dinah?

Where are her sons?

The men approach. Her husband and David Maynard.

Edmund, she implores, our boys?

She gazes at Edmund but he cannot speak.

Taken, Maynard says.

Taken?

Indians, he says.

Maynard catches her before she falls. They move inside, seat her beside the hearth, close the shutters, bolt the door. Gripping his gun, Edmund stares before him as though possessed.

In heaven's name, Husband, tell me, she begs.

It is Maynard who responds through barely moving lips.

Savages—eight or ten, maybe twelve. They took the boys—yours and Thomas's.

Did you not pursue them? Turning wildly from one man to the other, her voice rises to a shriek. Why did you not pursue them?

Dropping to his knees before her, Edmund clasps her hands.

If we had, Ruth, they would have killed the boys.

His voice breaks. Neighbor Maynard and I would have been here sooner...

He hides his face in her lap.

Maynard answers for him.

We stopped to bury Nahor, he says.

BOSTON, MASSACHUSETTS

On an unseasonably stifling day in late September 1704, His Excellency Joseph Dudley, Her Majesty's Governor for the Province of Massachusetts Bay, is taking advantage of his deputy's absence from their office in the Boston State House to loosen his elaborately tied cravat and remove his horsehair wig. What little sea breeze enters through the open window plays soothingly about his shaven head—and the governor needs soothing. The European war that has spread to the New World has given rise to the vexing problem of raids on the English settlements by the French government's Indian surrogates. These efforts to terrorize and depopulate his country's frontier are increasing, despite Dudley's frequent protestations to Governor Vaudreuil in Québec. More and more English men, women and children are being carried off, some to be adopted by their captors to replace tribal members who had died; some redeemed by missionaries, baptized into the Catholic faith, and placed in seminaries or convents; some becoming servants in French or Dutch households; some few imprisoned or left to go free. Many English families do everything possible to redeem their relatives, and this is the problem that the governor is finding most troubling. Indians often sell their captives to French middlemen who, in turn, demand ransoms from the distressed families. Unscrupulous merchants in New France profit from this trade, and Dudley has implemented measures to combat it since taking office. Most recently, he has written to Vaudreuil demanding considerate treatment for the English captives and proposing that a system of prisoner exchange be put in place to eliminate ransom. He also communicates frequently with Peter Schuyler, the respected Indian commissioner in Albany, on whose network of informants Dudley relies for warnings of attacks in time for the inhabitants of frontier towns to set up defenses.

Now, adding to the pile already on his desk is yet another petition, not a "petition for relief" requesting monetary help for ransom, but one asking for permission to travel to Kahnawake, where the petitioner, Edmund Rice, hopes to redeem his sons and nephews taken by Indians from the settlement of Chauncy, a day's ride southwest of Boston.

Hearing footsteps approaching, the governor replaces his wig and straightens his cravat in time to present a composed face to the door and respond to the discreet knock with a gruff "Enter." Seeing that the visitor is his deputy, Robert Tenney, Dudley relaxes and motions him to be seated.

"Yet another petition, Tenney," he says, indicating the document before him on the desk, "but I intend to stand firm in never allowing the payment of ransom money to savages. We cannot allow our women and children on the frontier to be bargained for like cattle or beaver."

"Indeed, sir, trading in English citizens would seem to have become more lucrative than furs," says Tenney.

"And with the escalation of this war, the evil is likely to worsen," Dudley responds. "I am presently drafting a letter to Vaudreuil reiterating our request to exchange English captives for the French prisoners we are holding. If he agrees to the terms, this ignoble state of affairs will come to an end."

"Respectfully, sir, I contend that such an agreement will not entirely resolve the problem of captives in Indian hands," says Tenney. "As Governor Vaudreuil stated in a recent letter, he has no control over those unfortunates who can only be released from captivity if they wish it and their Indian masters allow it."

"That may be the case in this latest abduction," replies the governor, handing Edmund Rice's petition to Tenney. "However, as no exchange treaty has yet been negotiated with New France, I am inclined to grant this man's request. Draft a reply to him, if you please, and dispatch it to Chauncy by an early post. Let us pray that the Rice boys' captors will allow them to return to their families."

CHAUNCY, MASSACHUSETTS

The snow lies thick about the house on Powder Hill. It is mid-January. Almost six long months have passed since the boys were ripped from their families, and Edmund Rice is leaving to go in search of his sons and nephews. Deep lines mark his face, and Ruth's brown hair is streaked with white. A musket stands loaded in a rack beside the heavy wooden door, which Edmund has reinforced with iron cross-bars.

"How long will you be gone, father?" asks Dinah, her head against his chest. "I sorely miss Silas and Timothy."

For her mother's sake, she does not mention Nahor. They have been only once to lay flowers on the place near the flax fields where he is buried, for there is now another grave to tend—the cradle beside the fire is empty, and Moses lies beneath the ground beyond the kitchen garden.

"I will be home in the spring," he says, clasping her to him. "Look after your mother and sister, my daughter."

Crouching down, he calls little Huldah, folds her in his arms. Ruth hands him his heavy wool cloak. His haversack holds food for the four-day walk to Deerfield. From there, he and Ensign John Sheldon will set out on foot for their three-hundred-mile mission to Kahnawake.

A last long embrace. "You remember how to load the musket, Ruth?" She nods. "Should you have cause to fire it, our neighbors will come to your aid." She nods again.

He lifts his felt hat from its peg, flings his cloak about his shoulders, and starts down the hill. He does not trust himself to look back.

Keeping him in view until he vanishes into the woods, Ruth closes the door.

New France

(four months later)

Kahnawake, the 8ᵗʰ day of February, 1705

My dear brother,

News reached us some time ago of the terrible losses our army suffered at Blenheim and of the capture of Marshall Tallard. I am greatly concerned for your welfare, but must perforce contain myself in patience until I hear from you.

Truly, Étienne, the trials that I experience in my mission in New France differ greatly from those I had anticipated. To me, as to all Jesuits, slavery is an abomination not to be tolerated, yet politics force us to be complicit in the taking of captives, many of whom lose their freedom in the service of their Indian captors, or in the households of white settlers, whether French or Dutch. Others—God be praised!—accept the light of our true faith, but in the violence that wrests people from their homes and destroys families, so many souls are lost that could have been saved. I pray daily for understanding.

I hope that my previous letter has reached you and that my long account relating to Timothy was of interest to you. While the circumstances of his arrival at Kahnawake were barbaric, I recall that you once witnessed a soldier being forced to run a similar gauntlet of his peers, and beaten to the point of death for insubordination, from which it is clear that infidels hold no monopoly on savagery. Our race, which professes to love Christ, is far indeed from following His Way.

I am responsible for the spiritual welfare of several other captives, but Timothy's soul has a quality that demands careful nurturing into accepting the fire of the Blessed Sacrament. It is clear that the boy was much affected by his exposure to the natural world on his long journey to Kahnawake, and his awareness of the manifestations of the Creator's glory may prove to be a portal through which he will be drawn to true godliness. I also believe that the failure of his Protestant God to bring his father to rescue him and his companions when they were abducted has cast doubt on the truth of the heresies with which he was early imbued. Although so far he has remained true to his Protestant beliefs and deaf to direct exhortations to renounce them, I believe I am beginning to see some curiosity concerning the mysteries of our holy faith. In this, I am greatly aided by Onatah. Her devotion to the Catholic sacraments is a daily example to him, and is diluting his former beliefs. I am thankful that, having won his confidence in my early meetings with him, he finds comfort in speaking with me, and now seeks me out of his own accord.

Some days ago, we sat before a window watching the snow as it drifted from the heavens.

"See, my son, how the love of God illuminates all things," I observed. "Though the sky is dark, yet the snow's gentle purity brings light. In its silence, all living things praise the Creator Who is ever mindful of their needs. Every tree, every plant, every seed, even the lowly moss, gathers strength at this time of rest that it may more joyfully participate in the glory of creation when it awakens in the warmth of spring. We humans, too, are asleep until we find the true path that God in his mercy has revealed to us and which alone leads to where He may be found. The seed of eternity that is within us responds with joy to the rain of God's love."

"Is there only one God?" he asked.

"There is only one true God."

"Is He the same God that my English father worships?"

"That is a false god, for the true God hears only the prayers of those who accept His Blessed Sacrament, venerate the saints, and believe in miracles as manifestations of His power."

Timothy sat in silence for a few minutes.

"Ontasaga says that our God and the Great Spirit of the Mohawk are the same because, if there is only one god as the white man says, then the Indians and the white men are worshipping the same god, only in different ways."

"Ontasaga is a good man, but he is not on the right path to glorify God."

"Why is your way the only way?"

"Humans are beings with many failings. Sin is natural to us. We need to be constantly reminded of our duty to God so that we do not stray from the path of righteousness. Catholics have an earthly father, the pope. Through Saint Peter, who was the first pope, the Holy Father is the inheritor of Christ's teachings and is therefore our guardian in this life. He guides our souls to heaven if we follow the way he has decreed. And now, my son," I said, rising, "I must prepare for Vespers. Did you know that if you accept the grace of baptism, you can choose a saint whose life will be an inspiration to you?"

He followed me through the door, and walked beside me in the waning light.

"Do you have a saint?" he asked.

"Saint Ignatius is a constant reminder to me of what a follower of Christ should be. I honor him every day, but especially on his feast day, which is the last day of July. He inspires me to be a good Jesuit."

"I want to be a good hunter. Is there a saint for that?"

"There is. His name is Hubert, and he is celebrated on the third day of November."

We had reached the church. Timothy turned to go back to his longhouse, and as I opened the door, he looked over his shoulder at me and smiled.

When the time came for Timothy to put aside his English identity, the tribal elders gathered at Oserohkoton's grave. In an atmosphere of great solemnity, I watched as women plucked out his hair leaving only a topknot, which they adorned with feathers. After painting his face and body with sacred symbols, and hanging a belt of wampum about his neck, they pierced and ornamented his nose and ears, then led him to a ritual bath in the river. His whiteness having been symbolically washed away, his adoptive mother, Onatah, dressed him in clothes made of skins. Elders then led him in silence to the council house, where they presented him with a pipe, a tomahawk, and a flint and steel. The council fire was lit, revealing members of the tribe, their faces and bodies ceremonially decorated with paint, seated in circle around him. After all had smoked the pipe, the chiefs welcomed him into the Turtle Clan and the tribe. At the great feast that followed, Ontasaga proclaimed that Timothy had taken the noble place of Oserohkoton (meaning 'he passes through the year'), by which name he is now known. With a dignity beyond his years, he took his place in the circle with the male members of his new family. His brother, Silas, was received into the tribe at the same time, and now bears the name Tannhahorens ('he splits the door').

The solemnity of the ceremony affected Timothy/Oserohkoton profoundly. The process of shedding his past had brought memories rushing in. He came to me the next day, wishing to tell me what was in his heart.

"When Onatah hung the sacred wampum about my neck, it felt somehow alive and seemed to fill me with the spirits of the ancestors. But I do not wish to forget my English family, especially my mother, and I would be sad if she did not remember me."

"You will always be a part of her, my son, and she will always hold you in her heart. At the time that you accept God's grace, I will teach you to pray for her."

"I would like to pray for Ashur and Adonijah too. At night I cannot sleep because I wonder what has happened to them. Have they also been adopted into a tribe? Or perhaps they are slaves, maybe even dead. How can I find out, Father?"

I promised him that I and my *confrères* would make enquiries, assuring him that if we could determine where they are, we would try to redeem them. Nodding his head in acknowledgment and thanks, he left to join his companions in the village.

It is gratifying to know that my experiences in the New World, limited though they have been, are of interest beyond our family, and that you are judicious in what you make known to others. Foremost in my concern, though, will ever be to maintain the link with you and our mother through my writings. May God bless and keep you both.

Yours in Christ,

Vincent, S.J.

Touraine, France

At the Abbey of Fontevraud, the 4th day of April, 1705

My dear son,

Prepare yourself for news that I can barely set to paper due to the trembling of my heart and hand.

Three days ago your brother arrived at the abbey in a farm wagon. I had received no tidings of him since the great battle that destroyed our army last year, and had thought him dead. He is so much altered from the suffering he has endured that I scarcely knew him. In short, Vincent, he survived, but at great cost. He told me that thousands of his fellow officers and their horses had drowned in the River Danube. Miraculously, he, together with a small group of horsemen on the flank of the main body of fleeing cavalry, was forced over a cliff into a marshy ravine. His horse broke two legs and fell upon him, but Providence and the soft earth preserved him. He lay thus, unable to move and barely conscious, for a day and a night.

His life was spared at the cost of his left leg, which was amputated above the knee. His left arm, too, was badly damaged. He surely would not have survived the brutal surgery at the field station if he had not been taken to a nearby monastery shortly afterwards, where the good Benedictines tended his wounds with Christian charity and their knowledge of healing herbs. They also straightened his arm, which had been badly set. He remained at the abbey until he had recovered sufficiently to travel. Over many agonizing weeks, and through the aching months of winter, he made his way here by the kindness of strangers, who offered him shelter, sustenance, and transport. He and I will remain at Fontevraud until he has fully recovered his strength.

Besides his physical pain, he suffers agonies of spirit regarding Marie-Céleste Rambouillet, to whom he was secretly affianced before leaving to join his regiment. Dread of how she will receive him hampers his recovery, yet his determination to carry out his duty to her, our family and the people dependent on our estate remains strong within him.

I know this news will affect you deeply, Vincent, and perhaps give rise to thoughts of returning to France. I hasten to assure you that there is no need to deviate from your chosen path. Once Étienne and I are home, we will obtain an artificial limb for him, and with the help of our admirable steward, our estate will flourish once again. For now, I praise God every minute of every day for preserving my son's life.

I wish you to know how much your letters mean to me. Through them, I feel as though I accompany you as you follow your mission in the New World, so vividly do you portray its people and your experiences.

Ever your loving mother,

Aurélie

LETTER SIX

New France

(five months later)

Kahnawake, the 18th Day of July 1705

My dear Étienne,

Knowing the turbulent state of Europe, I cannot but be apprehensive as to your welfare, and am hoping that the long silence on your part is attributable only to your many duties as an officer. My thoughts often drift to those peaceful years when we were able to attend plays and concerts with Mother. I remember particularly her pleasure at a performance of *Tartuffe*, and there are times when I sorely miss the cultural life of France. I am, however, fortunate in being able to discuss many subjects of interest with Fathers Jacques and Pierre, and my soul rejoices on the rare occasions when I have the opportunity to play my flute. When your affairs are more settled, and you can find a suitable courier, my *confrères* and I would benefit from, and greatly appreciate, a parcel of books from our father's collection, in particular Descartes' *Discourse on Method* and any others that you do not wish to retain.

You will, I believe, be interested to know that Oserohkoton seems completely at home among his peers. Indian children run wild. They are never disciplined, learning only by example. Captive children find this much to their liking, and Oserohkoton is no exception. As he is quick to learn, this spring the older boys taught him to steer a canoe while they fish, and how to set a trap. Indeed, yesterday he proudly presented me with a hare he had caught. He is also becoming accustomed to the Indian food prepared by Onatah, her groundnut stew and corn pancakes fried in bear grease being now as delicious to him as his English mother's apple turnover and oatcakes once were.

In late February, when Oserohkoton had been settling in to his new identity as a Mohawk boy, Father Jacques came to my room with disquieting news. "Vincent, prepare to meet with the father of your catechumen. Edmund Rice, in company with Ensign Sheldon of Deerfield, came yesterday to Kahnawake in search of his sons and nephews. The men had the foresight to petition Governor Vaudreuil for permission to ransom Oserohkoton and Tannhahorens, as well as some of the Deerfield captives. They received his consent, on condition that the Mohawks and the captives were willing. Ontasaga has said that he and Onatah do not wish to hold Oserohkoton here against his will, so the decision will be the boy's. Father Pierre and I at first denied the heretic access to his son, but Governor Vaudreuil insists that we accede to his request. We have therefore given our consent, on condition that you are present at any meeting between father and son."

Shortly before my regular time of meeting with Oserohkoton, Mr. Rice came to the common room of our quarters. Still weary from his long journey, which I could envision with clarity from my own harsh experience, I invited him to be seated near the fire. He courteously but coldly refused, saying that he preferred to remain standing.

"Is my son well?" he asked.

"He is in excellent health," I replied, "both physically and spiritually."

His jaw tightened.

"Has he remained true to the faith of his forefathers?"

"He recites his catechism."

A knock at the door put an end to this questioning. I opened it to find Ontasaga and Oserohkoton without. When the boy saw who was with me in the room, he froze on the threshold. Gazing as if in a trance, dwarfed by his father, his adoptive father, and his spiritual Father, he stood alone, his small figure remote from us all. Edmund Rice, too, was transfixed. In nothing but the boy's eyes could he discern his son. The light hair dressed in barbarous fashion and darkened with bear grease, the face disfigured with paint, the body clothed in savage garb, all concealed the boy's former identity.

The father took a step towards his son.

"Timothy?"

The boy turned his face away.

"You did not come," he said. "I prayed to God every day, but you did not come."

"God heard you, my son. I am here now. Return home with me. Your mother awaits you anxiously."

The boy stood for endless minutes, head bowed. Then, looking at his father directly for the first time, he said in a clear voice, "This is my home."

The man blanched.

"You are my son. Your place is with our family. We love you and need you." Turning to Ontasaga and me, he said through clenched teeth, "You are demons who have perverted my son away from his family and his faith with your heathen superstitions and damnable doctrines." Ontasaga, understanding the contempt if not the words, took a step toward the Englishman, fist raised. With a look and a gesture, I deflected him from his purpose, whereupon Mr. Rice addressed himself directly to me, saying, "I demand to see my son alone."

I told him that would be impossible, but wishing to allow Oserohkoton the opportunity to speak with his father so that he might not later have regrets, I asked Ontasaga to leave us. I then seated myself unobtrusively on the opposite side of the room. In a low voice, Mr. Rice questioned his son earnestly as to whether he was faithfully reciting his catechism and reading his scriptures. Oserohkoton replied that he was trying his best.

"Remember, my son, that our prayers are heard only by God. Nowhere in His Word has He told us that the saints have that power."

"*Your* God," said the boy (the father flinched) "did not hear my prayers when we were taken away."

Seeking closer contact with his son, Mr. Rice then told him about the people at home. The boy seemed interested, particularly concerning his mother, but was more troubled about the fate of Ashur and Adonijah. The father assured him that he would do everything possible to redeem them, whereupon I heard the child say, "You didn't come to rescue *us* and you let Nahor be killed." A bitter blow indeed. The father's shoulders slumped. Putting his hand on the boy's head, he said, "I will go now, my son. Above all, I ask that you recite your catechism." With that he turned towards the door without a glance at me, and was gone.

I later heard that Tannhahorens, too, had refused to return with his father.

I would be less of a man, Étienne, if I did not feel compassion for Mr. Rice, misguided though he is. To brave three hundred miles in the depth of winter in search of your sons only to have them reject you must be one of life's cruelest torments. Yet this is the lot of a good number of captives' fathers. Puritan children, accustomed to daily strictures on their freedom and frequent reminders of their innate sinfulness, readily 'symbolize' (to use the Puritan expression) as Indians, embracing the customs of their new families, and refusing to return to New England when the opportunity occurs.

The connection to our family and homeland through your letters is priceless to me. Please assure our mother that I daily remember the wise guidance and love with which she has ever blessed our lives.

Yours in Christ,

Vincent, S.J.

I was about to seal this package when the courier who is to bear it to Quebec arrived and handed me Mother's letter. Étienne, dear brother, I am struggling to grasp the news of your injury. My heart is in turmoil for what you have suffered, but my soul is exalted in gratitude that your life was spared. Though I know you are in God's hands, I cannot but long to assist you and our mother and to be of closer comfort to you both. O that there were a way to cross the ocean like a bird that I might embrace you, however briefly! I shall await news of how you are faring with the keenest anticipation.

The courier is impatient to be gone. May you and Mother find comfort in God's love and in mine.

CHAUNCY, MASSACHUSETTS

It is spring when John Sheldon and Edmund Rice approach Deer-field. Mayflowers and anemones, bloodroots and hepaticas, brighten the edges of paths but they bring no joy to Edmund's heart, for it is here that he must bid farewell to his companion. He dreads the four-day journey to Powder Hill alone with his thoughts and fears. How will he tell Ruth that their boys, their beloved sons, refused to come home with him? How to bear the suffering that such news must cause her? Resolutely, he sets out.

Dinah is the first to see him.

Mother! Mother! Father is coming up the hill! Come quickly, mother!

Are the boys with him?

I do not see them, mother. Perhaps my brothers are tarrying in the woods.

They hurry down the path. One look at his face and she knows the worst.

The savages would not release them? asks Ruth.

Edmund bows his head. They did not wish to return, he says.

A look of shocked incredulity.

How can that be? A low keening escapes her lips. That cannot be. It cannot!

He looks up with fierce anger in his eyes, slams a fist into his hand.

Our sons hold me responsible for their capture, Ruth—me, their father!--because I was powerless to rescue them.

His voice breaks.

They are lost to us. They no longer recite their catechism. The pope's accursed minions have perverted them from their faith and they have no defense against the superstitions of the infidels.

Ruth turns away. He reaches out to her, but she is beyond comfort, beyond grief. First Nahor, then Moses, and she felt her heart would break—but this cruel rejection tears at her vitals.

Are my brothers not coming back? asks a small voice behind the parents as they approach the house on Powder Hill.

We must forget them, comes the father's sere reply.

But a mother cannot deny the corners of her heart where love of each child has taken root. Beside Moses' grave are two stone cairns that, in the warm months, are always garlanded with flowers.

NEW FRANCE

(FIVE MONTHS LATER)

Kahnawake, New France, the 1st day of December 1705

Étienne, dear brother,

My happiness today on receiving a letter from you was joyfully increased by the tidings that you are to marry Marie-Céleste Rambouillet. That she has embraced your changed circumstances with the devotion of a true heart does not surprise me, for I remember her as a child of unusual piety and understanding. I was delighted with the resourcefulness evident in her proposal that, until you are more comfortably able to ride a horse, you acquire a pony cart to convey you and our steward in your inspections of the estate. There is no doubt that she will be a steadfast partner though all the joys and vicissitudes that lie ahead. I have deep satisfaction, too, in knowing that the relationship between Marie-Céleste and our mother is one of respect, harmony and affection. How appropriate it is that the families of de Surville and Rambouillet will at last be united through your marriage to the sister of the girl who reigned in my heart before I found the love of Christ!

Here in the New World, the opportunities for glorifying His Holy Name continue to be a source of satisfaction as well as frustration to me, particularly in my work with the Puritan heretics. In their blindness, they see themselves as victims of Satan's wiles and passive recipients of God's grace, not as instruments of His power in the fight against evil. The Deerfield captives, in particular, are notable for their steadfastness in refusing to turn to our faith. Most recalcitrant among the adult captives is John Williams, their prideful minister. Since he was redeemed by Governor Vaudreuil on his arrival in Montreal last year, he has been living in a village east of Québec. His son, Stephen, recently redeemed from his Abenaki master by Governor Vaudreuil for forty crowns, has been reunited with his father. During his eighteen months of captivity, the boy briefly embraced the light of our faith. Appalled by this lapse, Rev. Williams is determined to prevent our "machinations" in turning captives, especially children, from their Protestant faith, and has come several times to Kahnawake. He is particularly concerned for the spiritual welfare of his daughter, Eunice, now eight years old, and 'symbolizing' strongly as Indian.

Due to the influence of Reverend Williams, who, I discovered, had met with Oserohkoton without my knowledge, the boy remains wary of embracing our faith. Another vexing complication is that Ontasaga confuses him with native beliefs. Some weeks ago, he asked me whether I believe in the truth of dreams, to which I replied that I am guided only by truths conveyed to me by the Holy Spirit through the Bible.

"But Ontasaga says that our souls go on long journeys while we sleep," he said, "and that dream symbols are messages from the soul. If we do not try to understand and follow their meaning we will not have a good life."

"The only way to find the good life is to follow the path of righteousness, my son. The symbols that arise when we are asleep and unaware of God's guidance are devices of Satan to turn us from that path."

Lifting his chin defiantly and striding past me, he paused at the door. "Who should I believe, Father?"

His confusion is understandable, Étienne, and, not wishing to distress him further, I ignored his question. With a smile, I said, "Are you not soon to be nine years old? I recall that when we first talked you told me that your birthday falls on the fifteenth day of September."

"I take no note of such things anymore," he said, not meeting my gaze.

"I am required to go to Montréal on that day. I thought you might like to accompany me. We will visit the priests at Saint Sulpice and the nuns at the hôtel-Dieu. It may be that they will have news of Ashur and Adonijah."

He looked up at me, eyes shining. "Of all things, that is what I would like," he cried.

"I will seek Onatah's permission for you to accompany me," I replied.

I was well satisfied when that permission was granted. For Oserohkoton, it heralded an adventure that appealed to his natural curiosity. For me, it provided an opportunity to strengthen the bonds between us, and to establish contact with the nuns and priests in Montréal. In particular, I hoped to make the acquaintance of Henri-Antoine Mériel de Meulan, a Sulpician priest of infinite merit, whose success in making conversions has been remarkable. The possibility of bringing Oserohkoton into his orbit was thus of great interest to me.

The town of Montréal is situated on an island. We went by canoe up the Saint Lawrence River, and as we approached the harbor, I heard Oserohkoton catch his breath. I turned to see him, body rigid, gazing in awe at the sailing ships at anchor, or, with wind-filled sails, preparing to set out to sea.

"Those are ships, are they not, Father?"

When I replied in the affirmative, a shadow of sadness touched his face.

"My mother—my English mother—showed me a picture of one once. She said my grandfather sailed across the ocean in such a ship a long time ago." After a pause, he asked, "Have you ever been on a ship, Father?"

"I came from France in a fine *barque* such as that," I said, pointing to a three-masted vessel coming into port. "It took many weeks to get here."

"I should like to see the lands across the sea, especially England," he said. Then, squaring his shoulders as if to confront the reality of his situation, he turned to look at the town.

Montréal straggles along the edge of its harbor, from the hill for which it is named at the north, to the hôtel-Dieu marking its southern limit. Five spires punctuate its skyline, and although the town is barely larger than Kahnawake in both population and extent, to the boy's untutored eyes, it was a metropolis. As we neared the wharf, his excitement grew.

"Are there no longhouses in Montreal, Father? Is this a city like Tours where you came from? I see churches, but are there palaces?" The questions tumbled from his lips, and I answered them as best I could, this being my first visit to Montréal.

As we neared the wharf, and having been warned about the debauchery of many of the town's residents, I gazed with some dismay at the throngs of ruffians through which we would have to pass. On landing at the *quai* I searched among the crowd for the most respectable-looking man from whom to ask directions as I wished to take a route that would preserve Oserohkoton from witnessing the town's worst elements. Standing apart from the seamen loading or unloading cargo amid curses and profanity, fur traders bargaining with buyers, Indians and soldiers lolling on barrels and bales, and alcohol purveyors urging all to purchase their accursed wares, stood a man serenely regarding the chaos. From his clothing, I perceived that he was a Dutchman. I addressed him in French, but he replied with such an execrable accent that I asked whether he spoke English. He nodded, and after giving me directions to the hôtel-Dieu and the seminary of Saint Sulpice, I enquired what business brought him to Montréal.

"I await a shipment of pelts from the north," he replied.

I had heard that the French and English fur trade was suffering because the Dutch were willing to pay elevated prices for beaver. Thus, not wishing to engage in a controversial discussion, I thanked him, and turned to go.

Putting a hand on my arm, he enquired, "And what might be your mission in Montréal, Father?"

"I am here concerning the welfare of English captives."

"Then you are in luck. An envoy sent by Peter Schuyler of Albany arrived yesterday. It may be that he will have news of those few who were taken to that town."

Following the Dutch trader's instructions, Oserohkoton and I avoided the street where taverns and houses of ill repute attracted the more dissolute of the citizens and natives. Traversing the main commercial thoroughfare, where Oserohkoton gaped at the sight of bewigged Frenchmen negotiating with semi-naked and painted Indians, we emerged into an area of substantial houses owned by the nobility of Montreal. The sight of pigs and cows roaming freely among the passers-by elicited delighted exclamations from the boy, who, not having seen such beasts since leaving his Massachusetts home, slowed our pace as he got his fill of them. Our progress was further hampered by my companion's curiosity, especially concerning a horse and carriage standing outside one of the mansions, such fine equipages being unknown to him. At last, just after noon, we arrived at the door of the hôtel-Dieu on the rue Saint Paul. It is an impressive stone building established in 1645 as a refuge for the sick, the poor and orphans by Jeanne Mance, a nurse called to the missionary life in a vision. She enlisted the services of the Religious Hospitallers of Saint Joseph, who continue to give succor to the neediest. English captives, mainly women and children, are placed there by our compatriots who, in compassion, and diligent in their desire to aid in saving souls, ransom them from the Indians. Through the sisters' kind offices, and aided by the patronage of several noble and devout families, many Protestants have thus been brought to the truth of our faith.

After paying my respects to the Superior, who, to my regret, was unable to provide any news regarding Ashur and Adonijah, I prayed with some of the captive women and children while Oserohkoton satisfied his hunger in the refectory. We then hastened to the seminary of Saint Sulpice, where I was eager to meet with Father Mériel.

When we arrived, I stood some minutes admiring the building's classic symmetry that reflects the Sulpicians' standing as *seigneurs* of the island of Montréal. A triangular pediment featuring the order's coat-of-arms on a red background links the stone posts of the entrance gate, which opens onto a courtyard. While my eyes were drawn to the fine Ionic portal and other architectural details, Oserohkoton exclaimed on seeing the clock situated on the roof between two dormer windows, and surmounted by a carillon of bells and a cross. Just then the hands of the clock moved to the hour of three, and the bells rang for the Divine Office of None.

Entranced, he listened until all was quiet, then turned to me.

"I did not know clocks could be so big, Father. I would very much like to know how they count the hours. My Uncle Thomas had a small one that looked like a lantern. He said his father brought it from England."

"Father Pierre has a clock for determining the times for the Divine Offices," I said. "Perhaps one day he will show you its mechanism."

With that he was content, and, passing through the gate, I rang the bell beside the main door. The servant who admitted us indicated that Father Mériel would meet with us when he had finished his devotions.

Within the half hour, Father Mériel, a man of magnetic energy whose openness of expression was immediately engaging, strode into the room.

"I bid you welcome, Father," he said. "It is some years since Father Jacques and Father Pierre honored us with a visit, but we often have news from Kahnawake. Their success among the Mohawk is echoed by ours among the heretics. And this," he said, turning towards the boy, "is a young catechumen, I presume."

"Not as yet, Father," I replied. "This is Oserohkoton, the adopted son of Chief Ontasaga. He came to us last year as a captive. He is most anxious to discover the whereabouts of his cousins, captured with him. We know that here at Saint Sulpice you keep detailed records of all captives who come to your notice. We are hopeful that Ashur and Adonijah Rice may be among them."

"Those names do not come to mind, but I will peruse our records when I return from Notre Dame where I am to perform a marriage ceremony for two captives recently filled with the grace of baptism. Baron Longueuil and his lady, who ransomed them from the Indians, will be witnesses at the wedding and I cannot keep them waiting. Come," he said briskly, "a servant will show you to your quarters. Oserohkoton will be housed with several young captives currently in our care. I understand that you plan to undertake a three-day retreat with your brother Jesuits here in Montréal. Do you wish the boy to remain with us until your return?"

"That would be of particular advantage to him," I said with a meaningful glance, "and to me also, if it is of no inconvenience to you."

"None at all. I and my brothers are glad to be of service. Will you join us at Vespers, and in the refectory afterwards?"

"Most certainly."

"Then I will see you in the chapel at sunset."

With a courteous inclination of his head, he left us.

Early the following morning, anxious to start the retreat, I made my way to the modest residence of the Jesuit community. The period of contemplation in company with my brothers was a blessing marred only by an incident on the last day. While making my way to Mass, I saw a priest dragging a young Puritan captive toward the church.

"The stench of your vice sickens me," he hissed through clenched teeth. "You will accept the truth of our faith or be returned to the savages." Reaching the door of the church, he pushed the boy into the sanctuary, saying, "Kneel, agent of the demon." Greatly disturbed, I confronted the priest.

"My brother, let the boy go. The seed of eternity exists in all humans. It blooms only through love, and instruction in the mysteries of our holy faith."

"This boy is sullied beyond redemption," he stuttered in fury. "He refuses to recant his heresies and infects us all with the contagion of his beliefs. Who are you to instruct me?"

"I am a humble servant of God," I said calmly, my eyes meeting his incensed gaze. "The Creator, in His wisdom and compassion, holds none to be beyond redemption. Only love can reveal the falsity of heresy. Examine your conscience through prayer that you may discern the right path to glorify God and to serve Him. I will pray that you find peace in your heart through contemplation of the holy Eucharist." So saying, I entered the church. At the conclusion of the Mass, I observed him still kneeling before the altar.

On returning to Saint Sulpice, I sensed a subtle change in Oserohkoton. Eyes shining, he declared as soon as he saw me, "Father Mériel found out that Adonijah was sold to a Frenchman who has a farm near Montreal, and a man who was staying here told him that Ashur is somewhere in that town called Albany. One day I shall go down the river and find him. And, Father," he continued more solemnly, "Father Mériel explained to me why miracles are important."

Thus, delicately, opens the flower of faith.

I trust that my ramblings continue to be of interest to you, Étienne. Do not be concerned if my letters are less frequent from now on. As time passes, it is becoming necessary for me to relieve my *confrères* of some of their duties. I am also devoting more hours to learning the subtleties of the Mohawk language. For my part, I read your accounts of our family and homeland with the greatest attention and gratitude.

Yours in Christ,

Vincent, S.J.

LETTER EIGHT

New France

(TWELVE MONTHS LATER)

Kahnawake, New France, the 2nd day of December 1706

Dear Étienne,

With another major defeat at Ramillies, it is a sad time indeed for our motherland. Such carnage cannot long be sustained. Despite the terrible price you paid, I daily give thanks that our family need no longer fear for your safety, and rejoice to hear how well our vineyards are progressing under your supervision. If your negotiations with the Dutch prove successful, our estate should return to the prosperity it enjoyed when our father was alive, which will bring great satisfaction to our mother.

I was intrigued by your account of the artificial limb that is making it possible for you to move about reasonably efficiently. The mechanisms of the articulated foot and locking knee interest me greatly, being developments of concepts originating with Paré, of whom I am an admirer as you know. I can appreciate that even with a padded leather cuff it is uncomfortable to wear for any length of time, but doubtless with improvements in the lining, combined with changes in its shape from wear, it will become more serviceable in the future.

Here at Kahnawake, our population of heretics is much depleted, the lengthy negotiations between the governors of Massachusetts and New France having at last been concluded. As I mentioned to you in earlier letters, Governor Dudley has long deplored the offering of captives for ransom by the Indians and some French. He assigned blame for the origin of this practice on members of our order, who, in the earliest days of their mission in New France, offered gifts to Indians in order to be allowed to communicate with captives. (If this indeed be the case, the practice was doubtless a perversion of our order's intentions.) In place of this commercial traffic he proposed a plan for exchanging prisoners, which was eventually accepted by Governor Vaudreuil. The requirements of the agreement having been met in April, the indomitable Ensign Sheldon sailed for Boston with forty-four captives in May, and Reverend John Williams, accompanied by fifty-four captives left Kahnawake in September. His daughter, Eunice, was not among them. Despite his fervent pleadings, she refused to leave her Mohawk family.

This wholesale return to New England of captives taken not only from Deerfield but from other frontier towns, has created great discontent among the Indians. The Kahnawake chiefs are increasingly unwilling to remain our allies, declaring that their main purpose in participating in raids is to obtain captives, whom they regard as family members, and that unless they are allowed to keep them, they will, in their parlance, 'bury the hatchet' and refuse to call out their warriors at the behest of the French.

Oserohkoton has fully accepted his Mohawk family, and shows particular affection towards Onatah, who has always treated him most lovingly. He sometimes speaks of his former home in our daily meetings, but his use of English, being increasingly inadequate to express the details of his Indian life, is declining. However, my efforts to refine my knowledge of Mohawk mean that I am now fluent, and our ability to communicate in that language is making gratifying progress. In another welcome development that I attribute in some measure to the influence of Father Mériel's luminous faith, he is displaying more curiosity concerning the Mass. With him, I continue to refer to God and Jesus. With my Indian catechumens and neophytes, however, I am forced to use circumlocutions such as 'He Who made the world,' and 'He Who brings blessings.'

Among his peers, Oserohkoton is at ease, participating fully in their activities. One day in April, when a certain bush came into bloom signaling the start of the fish-spawning season, he excitedly informed me that he was going with a large group of boys and adults to set up a fishing camp on a river about ten miles from Kahnawake. Two weeks later, I met him trudging along the dusty pathway in company with a small group of boys that included his brother, Tannhahorens. Each carried a large basket on his back, suspended by a band around his forehead, and loaded with what I estimated to be about twenty pounds of smoked fish. Some women, carrying double that load, brought up the rear.

Oserohkoton deposited his burden at the door of Onatah's longhouse, then turned to me. "Tomorrow we're going back," he announced. "There are thousands of fish. You should come with us, Father. You could eat all the fish you want."

Being curious to observe how the Indians provide for their winter needs, I obtained permission for a two-day absence, and set off with my young companions after Matins the following morning. The long walk, besides being a welcome diversion from my usual round of duties, proved to be profitable in furthering Oserohkoton's journey to baptism. On several occasions he left his peers to trot alongside me, venturing questions that reflected his growing interest in our faith. Of particular concern to him was that many of his Mohawk companions believe that animals have spiritual qualities similar to those of humans, and that each race of animals has its own chief who rules over their worlds in the afterlife.

"What should I tell them, father?" he asked.

"Your answer should be that the souls of men, too, have a chief. Because men are above the animals, their chief, whom we call God, is supreme in the realm of spirits."

"So the pope you told me about speaks for God while we are on earth, but in the spirit world God is Chief of all our spirits, including the pope's?"

"That is true," I replied, well satisfied with his understanding and his eagerness to impart what he had learned to his cohort.

This interchange with Oserohkoton brought to mind the times you and I strolled through the countryside when you visited me at Rennes during my novitiate. How many companionable discussions arose, and how many values and interests we found we share! Walking, whether alone or in company with a kindred spirit, is a godly pursuit, for it relieves the mind of the common round of thought.

Arriving at the camp before sunset, we found that the activities of the day were abating, some women gutting and cleaning the remaining fish from the most recent haul, others threading them onto sticks and placing the bounty in a shelter tended by an old man who fed a fire with green alder and apple branches that produced a fragrant smoke. As the moon rose above the horizon, and after a welcome meal of fish stew, I gathered some boughs for a bed. Beneath majestic pines, I commended my soul to God, and slept soundly until sunrise.

Daylight revealed that there were about one hundred and fifty people in the camp. Emerging from the temporary shelters they had constructed from branches and elm bark, they wasted no time in setting about their duties. A few went off to gather wood, but most went down to the river. The men were chiefly concerned with tending the funnel-like traps they had constructed, while the boys' bountiful energy was put to good use by providing them with weighted cords that they dragged across the bottom of the river from the far bank to the shallows opposite, scaring the fish towards the women waiting to scoop them into baskets. As you can imagine, at that time of year the water was barely above freezing, but the boys, in their camaraderie and enthusiasm, seemed oblivious to the cold.

Leaving the camp when the sun was at its zenith, I returned to Kahnawake in welcome solitude. I sought out Father Cholonec to report my arrival, and was greeted with somber news.

"A report came yesterday from Father Louis d'Avaugour at the Lorette mission among the Huron. Father Aubanelle is gravely ill from a wound, and a surgeon is urgently needed. As you are the most experienced among us in that skill, I have offered your services. Prepare to leave at daybreak tomorrow. The Huron messenger will travel with you. I have arranged for you to go by canoe from Montreal to Québec, which should take about five days. From there it is but a ten-mile walk to the mission."

Our river voyage was uneventful, and as I walked from Québec to the mission, my thoughts turned to Fathers Jean de Brébeuf and Gabriel Lalemant, who were among the first to minister to the Huron. In 1649, they were captured by the tribe's deadly enemies, the Iroquois. Mocking the priests' preaching that the more one suffers on earth, the greater is one's heavenly happiness, the heathen 'baptized' their victims with boiling water and subjected them to fiendish ritual torture, which the holy martyrs endured with stoicism and acceptance in the name of Our Savior.

Although I had been informed that the Lorette mission was small, I was not prepared for its obvious poverty. I made my way to the church, where a young Huron passing by showed me to Father d'Avaugour's quarters. While I refreshed myself with a simple meal, he told me how Father Aubanelle's wound came about.

"In our village," he said, "nobody is buried within the precinct of the church. This is well known to all our Indians, yet three weeks ago one man, who thrives on making trouble, came to Father Aubanelle and insisted that his kinswoman be interred within the building. Seeing the Father's refusal as an insult to his clan, he swore to take revenge. Running to his cabin he reappeared with a bow and arrows. Several ill-aimed missiles struck Father Aubanelle, but were deflected. As he extended his arm in a plea to his assailant, an arrow entered at his wrist, penetrating to the elbow. Father Aubanelle removed the shaft, but the arrow head remained embedded near the joint. Blood spurting from the wound, he fell to his knees and appealed for help, whereupon several women ran to his assistance. One, with admirable presence of mind, applied pressure to his upper arm, greatly staunching the flow of blood, then bound the wound tightly. His relief from the initial pain was short-lived. His arm started to swell, the pain reached unbearable intensity, and a fever set in. That is the condition you will find him in now."

In company with Father d'Avaugour, I made my way to the injured priest's quarters, his cries of pain reaching us before we entered his room. Tossing wildly on his bed, he begged for relief from his agony. Calmly, Father d'Avaugour knelt beside him and explained who I was and that I would help him.

I told the suffering man that before I could find the arrow head I would have to lance his arm. He gave his assent with a slight nod.

One of the women having provided me with a gourd in which to catch the blood, I placed a piece of wood between his teeth. Retrieving a lancet from my medical chest, I asked Father d'Avaugour to hold the patient as still as possible. I then pierced the injured man's grossly swollen arm, whereupon a large quantity of putrid blood welled out of the incision. Using a thin probe, and taking great care to avoid damaging sinews or another artery, I investigated the wound in the hope of locating the arrow head. On the third attempt, my instrument scraped against something that was not bone.

"I have found the head, father," I said. "When the swelling has subsided and you are better able to sustain further treatment, I will attempt to remove it."

After cleansing the wound as much as possible with alcohol from my supplies, and leaving it open so that it could drain further, I gave him a small quantity of brandy and water to bring down his fever. Exhausted, he then fell into a deep sleep.

You are all too familiar with the horrors inflicted by modern weaponry, Étienne, but arrows bring problems of their own. I did not know whether the head was flint or steel, but both have sharp edges, making it impossible for tissue to heal around them. A metal head bent into a hook shape through impact with a bone, makes extraction particularly difficult. The conundrum facing me was that, given the morbid abscess, and if removal of the arrow head proved impossible, I would have to amputate Father Aubanelle's arm. For several days and nights I tended my patient, prayerfully building his strength with broth, and reducing his fever with cold cloths and weak brandy. Severe pain, unrelieved by small doses of laudanum, persisted. At the end of a week, judging him able to withstand further procedures, I lengthened the original incision, allowing me to insert my fingers and find the arrow head, which from its smoothness I determined to be metal. All attempts to remove it by hand were fruitless, the point being embedded in bone. My forceps proving to be no more effective than fingers, I asked one of the women to find me a length of wire. Carefully threading this behind the arrow head at the narrow part, and, twisting the strands together firmly to form a loop, I pulled with all my strength. The head came free, at which there was great rejoicing among the women. Having fallen into a swoon, Father Aubanelle was unaware of my success, but from that time on, with God's help, his recovery was assured.

When not tending my patient, I had many discussions with Father d'Avaugour. He told me that the people in this small village of one hundred and fifty souls and several similar communities in the area are but a remnant of the Huron nation that numbered perhaps twenty or thirty thousand, according to the first explorers and missionaries who came among them. Having observed that the crops grown by the villagers were sparse, I commented to Father d'Avaugour that it was apparent that the Huron were struggling to survive.

"That is sadly the case," he replied. "Besides suffering the ravages of the white man's diseases, they have been forced to move many times to avoid conflict with the Iroquois, whose attacks have all but destroyed them. In addition, they have had to contend with the greed of our merchants, whose rapacity in plying them with alcohol knows no bounds. Unless King Louis takes measures to curb this evil trade, the work of our missions to root out the tare of drunkenness is doomed." After a pause, he added, "The miserable patch of land you see here, granted to them by the beneficence of our government, is but a fragment of the vast tract that was once their homeland. These proud people, who for centuries were self-sufficient, have now been reduced to trading animal pelts and lumber in exchange for grains and vegetables."

This conversation left me much troubled in spirit, Étienne. It brought into focus questions that have long been heavy on my conscience. Begging leave to borrow Father Lalemant's *Relation* of 1642 from the mission's small collection of books, I retired to my quarters. There I sought the passages that are, I believe, the origin of my disquiet. The Father recounts that the Indians "observed, with some basis in reason, that since our arrival in these lands, those who were nearest to us happened to be those most ruined by the diseases and that the towns that welcomed us now appear utterly exterminated." He further acknowledges "that these poor people are in some sense excusable … For it has happened very often, and has been remarked more than a hundred times, that where we were most welcome and baptized the greatest number of people was in fact where the greatest number died." While he held that their "false imagination" allowed the savages to believe that we Jesuits had a "secret understanding with the disease," yet he confessed that "No doubt we carried misery with us, since, wherever we set foot, either death or disease followed us."

To calm my fevered thoughts, I sought the peace of the river bank.

CB BO

Are they the blessed seed from which future harvests will spring, these pitiful few who have survived and been converted to our faith? They are models of piety and virtue, exalting the holy fathers who prepared them to receive the sacraments of confession and communion. They excite the admiration of Europeans who witness in the so-called barbarians a devotion to the Lord Christ and the Holy Virgin that far exceeds their own.

Plainly, we Jesuits are God's agents in a plan that is beyond our understanding. How to reconcile Father Lalemant's observations with our mission to spread the Word of God? If it is His will to harvest an abundance of souls through baptism, the destruction of heathens in such numbers defeats that purpose. And if the holy Fathers were unwitting agents of Satan, did that demon turn their goodness to his own damnable ends by defiling them with a contagion that would spread among the people they came to save, thereby thwarting their sacred intention?

Or is it possible that the tens of thousands who died of pestilence were predestined souls fulfilling the will of God? If so, they were taken from this world before they had any knowledge of how to live righteously, which is surely unjust.

The early Fathers welcomed martyrdom joyfully, embracing their sufferings for His glory and His love. Whence will come consolation to my anguished soul?

അ ൠ

After several hours, as the moon and stars began their appointed journeys in the heavens, my disquiet dissipated in contemplating the wonder of His firmament. At last, when the sky brightened in the east, I made my way to the church, where a choir of women and children lifted their voices in a purity of sound that transported me to a sublime and timeless realm where God's love reigns supreme, unsullied by the unworthiness of humankind.

I have now tarried several weeks at Lorette. Father Aubanelle is gaining strength daily and has resumed most of his duties. Tomorrow I begin my journey back to Kahnawake, taking the opportunity to mail this letter in Québec.

May the Creator guide and protect you always, dear brother.

Yours in Christ,

Vincent, S.J.

New France

(ELEVEN MONTHS LATER)

Kahnawake, the 15th Day of November, 1707

I have allowed too much time to elapse since my last communication, Étienne. You and our family are, as ever, constantly in my prayers, but your September letter, which reached me in only two months and conveyed the news of your marriage, has spurred me to set pen to paper. I rejoiced to learn that your union was celebrated with appropriate solemnity, but also with festivities that included the people of our village. May your life with Marie-Céleste bring you contentment and the blessings of family. I take particular satisfaction in knowing that our mother is installed in her accustomed apartments, and that she continues to find companionship in the presence of your wife.

Earlier this year we received news of the Battle of Almanza, the outcome of which portends a Bourbon on the throne of Spain. In the past few months, raids on the English have diminished, but some minor sorties by Indians, unsupported by French forces, continue to yield a trickle of captives. Early in September, three children arrived at Kahnawake. Sarah, John and Zechariah Tarbell, being respectively fourteen, twelve and seven years old were taken from the town of Groton in Massachusetts. The girl was soon ransomed by a prominent family in Montréal and placed with the nuns at the hôtel-Dieu. The older boy was forced to undergo the trial of the gauntlet. Both he and his brother have since been adopted by our Mohawks. Oserohkoton, having turned eleven in September, regards John as a protégé to be instructed in the Mohawk ways.

Indeed, he is ever alert for opportunities to show initiative, and is becoming a leader among his peers. Tannhahorens is a quiet and thoughtful boy who, although the elder, is content to be Oserohkoton's follower. The brothers both show a particular aptitude for maneuvering a canoe, and it would not surprise me if they come early to the skill of negotiating rapids.

Be that as it may, all pales to insignificance in my catechumen's life beside his acceptance into our Holy Church. When it became apparent that he was ready to turn completely from his Protestant beliefs, he asked if I would name a day for his baptism.

"Could it be on the feast day of Saint Hubert, Father? I remember you told me that it falls on the third day of November."

"You remember well. Is your strongest earthly desire still to become a great hunter?"

"I would also like to be a great orator."

He sat silently for a while, then asked, "Father, can you tell me more about Saint Hubert?

You will recall the story from our childhood, Étienne—how Hubert, nobly born, hunted to excess, especially after his wife died in childbirth, until one day, when he was pursuing a magnificent stag, it turned to face him. Between its antlers was a crucifix, and he heard a voice which said, "Unless you turn to the Lord in holiness, hell will claim you in the afterlife."

Listening with rapt attention, Oserohkoton asked me what Hubert did then. I said that he did what the Lord commanded him to do: he sought out wise men who taught him compassion for animals.

He asked what that meant.

"He learned to shoot old animals when possible," I said, "and only when he was sure of killing them quickly; to take pity on sick or injured animals by putting an end to their suffering; and never to kill a female with young."

As I spoke, his face lit up, and he said, "But that is exactly what Ontasaga has taught me since I came to Kahnawake!"

"And that is why Saint Hubert is the perfect example for you to follow," I told him, "because by learning compassion for animals, he became compassionate towards people, too."

He wondered whether Hubert ever hunted again, and I replied that I did not believe he would have had the inclination to do so, because he gave all that he owned to the poor and dedicated his life to the worship of God.

"His experience with the stag also infused his spirit with such eloquence that he became famous for his sermons and was made a bishop."

"Father," he said, elated, "I will try to follow his example."

After a day of fasting and a night spent in vigil with me, Oserohkoton was ready to accept the Fire of the Blessed Sacrament on Saint Hubert's feast day. Before a congregation of our Christian Mohawks and in the presence of Father Jacques and Father Pierre, with Oserohkoton kneeling at the altar before us, I pronounced the words of baptism:

> *Let us embrace the Creed of our life-giving faith. To say the Credo with faith is to enter into communion with God, Father, Son, and Holy Spirit, and also with the Whole Church which transmits the faith to us and in whose midst we believe. This creed is the spiritual seal, our heart's meditation, and an ever-present guardian; it is the treasure of our soul.*

The moment when I made the sign of the cross on the boy's forehead with holy water, I felt a vibrant connection to Our Savior that continued as Oserohkoton accepted the Eucharist for the first time. At the end of the Ceremony of Acceptance, I was moved to pronounce a second century prayer:

> *Veni, creator Spiritus*   *Come, Creator Spirit*
> *mentes tuorum visita,*   *visit your love on us,*
> *imple superna gratia,*   *fill with highest grace*
> *quae tu creasti pectora.*   *the heart which you created.*

This letter will not reach you in time for Christmas, but my thoughts and prayers have no constraints of miles, or winds, or water. Know that they will be with you as you celebrate the birth of Our Savior. God grant that someday I may once again join my voice with yours in singing His praises.

Yours in Christ,

Vincent, S.J.

New France

(eleven months later)

Kahnawake, the 12ᵗʰ day of October 1708

My dear brother,

I have just received the joyful news that you are now a father and I an uncle, both of us doubly blessed in God's gift of twins. I was thankful to know that with His grace and the help of a skilled midwife, Marie-Céleste was brought safely through her long labor. That the girl is named Aurélie for our mother and the boy Vincent for me completes my felicity at the joy this event has brought to our family.

Alas, the war shows no sign of ending on either side of the Atlantic Ocean. At the insistence of our government, raids on English frontier towns have continued, but none so consequential as that on Deerfield. Then, early in July, some Indians who had participated in the destruction of that town told me they would soon be departing to join forces gathering for a significant attack on the village of Haverhill. They asked whether I would be willing to accompany their party. As I did not wish to be involved in another expedition conducted in so ignoble a way, I declined. I later learned that large numbers of Indians who had undertaken to support the French forces had abandoned the expedition, expressing reservations about warring against New England. Consequently, Hertel de Rouville, who was once again commanding our *troupes*, proceeded with only one hundred and sixty men, instead of close to four hundred as was originally planned. Yet again it was a slaughter of the innocents within the town, but fierce defense by the town's militia and those of neighboring settlements drove off the raiders, allowing some of the captives to escape and effecting the recovery of some of the loot. Reports estimated that thirty or forty villagers were killed or captured.

In January, rumors of an impending English invasion caused much apprehension in Québec. Thus, when Ensign Sheldon arrived that month on yet another mission to redeem captives, he and his delegation, which included Edmund Rice, were detained as possible spies. Mr. Rice's attempts to see his sons were of no avail as both Oserohkoton and Tannhahorens refused to meet with him. However, through the good offices of a certain Captain Lydias of Albany, Mr. Rice's negotiations on behalf of his brother to redeem Ashur were successful, and the boy, now fourteen years old, traveled home with his uncle. To Oserohkoton and Tannhahorens, this news was a great comfort.

Not long after mailing my previous letter, an event of considerable significance to me took place. At the commencement of the nine-day Midwinter Ceremony in January, which is the beginning of the Mohawk spiritual year and a time of new beginnings, Onatah, accompanied by a group of clan mothers, approached me after the early Mass.

"Father," said Onatah, "we Kanien'keha:ka have observed your willingness to understand and respect our ways. We value, too, your healing skills. You have not rejected the wisdom of our healers, but have often combined their knowledge with yours. I have consulted with my sisters of the Wolf and Bear, and they are of accord that the time has come for you to take your place in the Turtle Clan, and to accept a name that will unite you with our people. Accordingly, if you are in agreement, we will arrange a ceremony to take place at a propitious time during the next few days."

The festivities officially begin when messengers called "Big Heads," wearing braided cornhusk masks, visit each longhouse to stir the cold ashes with wooden mallets that are used to mash corn. This ritual is followed by others such as dream sharing, which is seen as a way to release troubled thoughts and detect diseases and mental disorders. The False Face Society, composed of men and women believed to possess spiritual powers, then meets to consult on how best to assist those in need of help. But, in keeping with the theme of new beginnings, this is also the time when newborns are welcomed into the tribe and given a name, and children transitioning into adulthood receive new names. Thus, in a solemn rite that combined traditional and Christian elements, I was adopted into the Turtle Clan, and now bear the name Otetiani, which means 'he is prepared,' in Mohawk. I am proud to be thus aligned with those I serve, for their barbarisms are amply balanced by their virtues. In their generosity and kindness to each other, their patience in adversity, their lack of ambition and avarice, it is evident to me, as it was to Father Paul le Jeune, one of the first to minister to the Huron, that the souls of all humanity arise from the same source.

My knowledge of the healing arts, though not extensive, are regularly called upon. Recently, I was troubled by my failure to relieve the suffering of a woman afflicted with lung fever. The remedies of a woman healer and the incantations of the shaman having proved ineffective, the patient had asked for my attendance. Feverish, laboring to breathe, and racked by coughing, she lay in the smoky gloom of her longhouse. Concerned more for the state of her soul than her body, I explained Heaven and Hell to her, and asked her where she would wish to go if she died. A woman who was standing nearby addressed me with indignation, saying that Indians would never give voice to such a matter as they always hoped that the afflicted person would recover. Ignoring this interruption, I told the sick woman that before God could bring about healing, she should be baptized. With a barely perceptible nod, she agreed. When at last I made the sign of the cross upon her brow, her spirit became calm, and she asked me to use the wisdom of the Black Robes to cure her. Having bled her to reduce the fever, I gave her a small amount of theriac and sugar from my meager supplies, which brought her comfort. Happily, she then fell into a deep sleep.

The following morning, I was chagrined to find my patient's condition had deteriorated during the night. I was told that, at her request, the village was preparing to play lacrosse to effect a cure. Known as Tewaarathon ('little brother of war') in the Mohawk language, lacrosse (thus named by early French settlers denoting a game played with a bent stick) is governed by rituals, and is often used to settle contentious matters between clans or tribes. My *confrères* told me that the year before my arrival at Kahnawake, a dispute with an Abenaki group over fishing rights had been settled in three days, on a field five miles in length. Perversely, the game is also considered a valuable cure for fevers and other diseases.

I recalled that Father Jean de Brébeuf, in his *Relation* of 1636, had spoken of this form of healing with great scorn, and, aware that our order disapproves of it as an aspect of native religion that runs counter to our Christian teachings, I approached Father Cholonec for permission to attend the match. Observing that my presence as a spectator would give tacit approval to a practice that is violent and encourages gambling, he nevertheless assented, saying that with greater knowledge of what is involved, I would more effectively be able to reason against its continuation. As the shaman oversees the rituals and the conduct of the game, I was particularly interested in observing him in order to be able to counteract his hold over our converts.

Lacrosse is played with sticks two to five feet long, bent into a circle at one end by steaming, the rings being filled with netting made of deer sinew. These implements are used to catch and fling a deerskin ball stuffed with hair against a rock or tree, or, in this case a post topped with a carved fish, at each end of the playing field. The evening before the game, about one hundred warriors, in full war paint and ceremonial regalia, and carrying their sticks, came before the shaman to be ritually prepared to play. Every participant then placed a wager on the result (gambling of all kinds being a favorite pastime of the Indians) with knives, beaded necklaces and beaver robes prominently displayed near the spectators as awards to the winners of each quarter. The concluding ceremony was a solemn, all-night dance in which participants sought divine support, for they believe the outcome to be supernaturally controlled.

The next morning, the teams made their way to the field, stopping frequently to conduct obscure rituals while uttering loud threats to intimidate their opponents. When I arrived at the area designated for the contest, I was told that the field extended for a mile beyond the palisade. For two days, from dawn to sunset, the players swarmed tirelessly in pursuit of the ball. In their efforts to approach close enough to fling it against the posts, players forcefully blocked their opponents with their bodies and sticks, paying no heed to injuries unless they were severe enough to send people off the field. Points were awarded according to the height at which the ball hit the post, a strike on the fish being the most valuable. For long periods the teams were invisible, play being temporarily confined to the far end of the field, but great was the excitement when the mob was seen moving in our direction.

At the end of the first day, I deemed myself sufficiently educated regarding the fundamentals of the game. Curious to ascertain how all this activity on her behalf was affecting my patient, I made my way to her longhouse, and was amazed to find her propped up on her sleeping platform and partaking of broth prepared by her clan sisters. She told me that my ministrations had brought weakness, whereas the lacrosse players had transferred their strength to her. The next morning, however, despite the continuing lacrosse game, all signs of recovery were gone. That evening, she died.

I have mused on this event, Étienne, because it seemed to me that the spiritual benefit to the woman of knowing she had the support of the entire community was a comfort in her final hours, allowing her to give up her soul in peace. The game was, I believe, a collective prayer, misdirected but sincere, that gave expression to the value placed on each individual within the tribe.

I had caught glimpses of Oserohkoton in the *mêlée* of the lacrosse game. Boys are encouraged to test their strength in such strenuous activities in preparation for the warrior life, and as a sturdy but lithe twelve-year-old, he is eager to participate in anything that will bring him closer to manhood. It appeared to me that he was well able to match the young braves in stamina, if not in skill. To the satisfaction of his clan, he is already bringing honor to the memory of his namesake. He not only works tirelessly to develop the physical prowess so valued by the Indians, but is accepted as a leader among his peers by virtue of his fairness in resolving disputes. Most remarkably in a boy his age, he shows an ability to master his passions and to endure discomfort and even pain without complaint. In his spiritual development, the seed has indeed fallen on fertile ground. He continues to ply me with questions, but the diligence of his devotions is a joy to behold.

You enquire whether I have found resolution in the matters that have long troubled my spirit. Penitence, and discussion with my confrères has brought me some relief, but I humbly continue to seek the discernment and understanding that comes only from the Most High through the intervention of the Holy Mother. I pray to be relieved from my doubts when it is His will, so that I may more perfectly follow the right path to glorify Him.

May Divine Providence guide and protect you always.

Yours in Christ,

Vincent, S.J.

NEW FRANCE

(TWENTY-SIX MONTHS LATER)

Kahnawake, the 15th day of December 1710

Knowing your generosity of spirit and depth of understanding, my dear brother, I am confident in receiving your pardon for my excessively long silence when I tell you that it arose from that spiritual malaise I referred to earlier, and from which I have only recently emerged. Doubtless you were concerned when you received no response to your last two letters, which I read with the greatest interest and gratitude. Let me hasten to assure you that on the physical plane, I am in robust health.

Praise be to God that our twins (for thus I think of them) survived rubeola almost unscathed, Vincent's loss of hearing in one ear being the least of the possible consequences of that dread disease. It pains me to think that in the midst of having to confront the hardships caused by last year's catastrophic frost that blighted Europe, you were further plagued by concern for the health of your children. May God forever bless our mother for her aid and succor to you all in that time of trial.

Human folly seemingly has no bounds, and I am thankful that thus far Tours has escaped the horrors of war. The drumbeats of destruction in Europe continue to reach us—Tournai, Malplaquet, Douai—the misery compounded by universal famine. You may have heard that New France recently suffered a significant *contretemps* in the loss of Acadia to the British. Combined with the disaffection of our Indian allies, the prospects for a French victory on this side of the ocean seem dimmer. Indeed, we lately heard that a delegation of four Indian chiefs—three Iroquois and one Mohican—has sailed to England to petition Queen Anne for help against our forces.

Kahnawake remains a peaceful haven, but we are not untouched by the normal vagaries of life. To the great sorrow of all who knew and venerated him, our beloved Father Chauchetière gave up his soul at Québec on April 17 of last year, having served at Kahnawake since 1677. His devotion to the Lord Christ and the Holy Virgin throughout his mission assured his awareness of God's love as he breathed his last, a blessing beyond price. In his place, we have welcomed Father Julien Garnier, who is eager to perpetuate and expand the work of his predecessor, including the preparation of some of Oserohkoton's peers for their initiation into adulthood. I, of course, am undertaking that task as it relates to Oserohkoton. Recognizing the value of many aspects of this heathen rite of passage, I am attempting to dilute some and enhance others with elements of our faith. Last year, when his voice began to change, Onatah's brothers accompanied Oserohkoton to a secret place in the woods, where they fasted for several days. On his return, his Mohawk grandmother presented him with a medicine bag containing protective herbs and a handful of earth. According to tradition, it should have contained his umbilical cord as a reminder of who he is, but this naturally was not possible in his case. I therefore counseled Onatah to place a small crucifix in the bag, which she was most willing to do, enclosing it in a leather purse lovingly embellished with a bead design representing the Virgin.

The purpose of this retreat is for the boys to experience visions of their guardian spirits or '*manitous.*'

og ຂo

Without self-mastery, says the wise man to the youths seated before him, the world is a wilderness ruled by invisible forces that seek power through a human agent. If you are a slave to the demons of anger and lust, jealousy and avarice, you are not fit to be called a man. In this life, it is our duty to perfect the body as well as the soul, in preparation for the day when we pass from this earth. The body is a reflection of the soul, he says. Through fasting and prayer, and by service to others, you will gain control over your bodies. Only then can your souls be led to awareness of the Great Mystery, allowing you to see clearly the path you are destined to follow. Its Voice will guide you to completeness of being in this world and in the realm of the ancestors.

Silently, the boys rise. They receive sacred headbands from their mothers, who accompany them to the river. There, in a farewell to childhood, the women brush their sons with pine boughs dipped in water; then, singing, they lead them to their 'uncles,' the elders of the tribe, who await the initiates at the entrance to the sweat lodge.

In the depths of the forest, many are the mysteries that reveal themselves to those who listen and see with the ears and eyes of the ancients. To them, the language of trees, the world of insects, the healing powers of plants, the lives of animals are at one with their spirits. To them comes understanding.

For three days Oserohkoton has not eaten, yet he feels no hunger. Each day, the elders impart more of the tribal mysteries, the legends that make the Kanien'keha:ka who they are. Each day he remains alone and silent, seeking the roots of his being.

Wearing only a breechclout, Oserohkoton leans with his back against a soaring pine, conscious of the pulsing life within. He senses the humble yet potent web beneath his feet—roots, rootlets, infinitesimal threads all serving the giant reaching toward the kingdom of light that they will never know.

The forest depths bring forth phantoms, too, wrenched to the surface of his awareness. The images rise, then slowly fade: his mother's face, at times smiling, at times sad, always tender; the hands of little Huldah and baby Moses as they wave goodbye; Dinah's grave and gentle gaze; his father's strong arms and worried eyes; Nahor ... He covers his face with his hands. The years have not dimmed the horror of that image. It must lie buried forever.

The fourth day, standing beneath the pine at dawn as life-giving rays filter through the tree-tops, a surge of gratitude and praise finds voice within Oserohkoton, a wordless song filled with vibrations of a world beyond the comprehension of the mind. As he gazes upward, arms wide, a majestic eagle, wings spread as if in brotherhood, draws his soul into its being. In their oneness, he becomes aware of a dove sheltering beneath the wings he shares with his guardian spirit, his 'manitou;' no ordinary dove, but one aglow with a light that enters his understanding as love.

Cß ഔ

All attempts to eradicate this practice having failed, my brother priests and I are resigned to attempting to place our neophytes' visions in a Christian context. Aware of our disapproval, and troubled that his 'uncles' had not been able to explain his vision to his satisfaction, Oserohkoton approached me shortly after his return from the woods. He told me that he had 'seen' an eagle, which, according to his elders, signified that he would be a warrior and a leader.

"What my uncles could not explain, Father, was that a dove was sheltering beneath its wings. It was not an ordinary dove, Father …"

My heart rejoiced for these symbols perfectly combined heathen and Christian beliefs.

"I believe that the vision of the eagle arose from the ancestors, my son, but Saint Hubert brought you the dove. Do you remember the story of the Great Flood that I told you some time ago? It was a dove that carried an olive twig to Noah as a sign that the storm was over and the earth ready to heal. Peace and hope returned to the world in the beak of a small bird, which has now appeared to you in its most holy form. You are indeed blessed, my son, for your *manitous* combine strength and gentleness, Christian and heathen. This bodes well for your future in the life of the tribe if you heed their wisdom."

After a long silence he diffidently added, "My uncles also taught me a prayer."

I asked him to repeat it to me.

"O Great Spirit of my fathers, help me to wholly void my heart of fear, and above all things, O God of my people and of my soul, help me to be a man."

As I could find no fault with this expression of trust in God, I indicated my approval, to Oserohkoton's relief and joy.

This was but one in many steps the Indians consider necessary on the path to responsible manhood. Believing that the body is a reflection of the soul, men seek to become worthy links in the lines of their ancestors through physical and mental perfection, which they see as precursors to being masters of themselves at all times. For some months, Oserohkoton's uncles have roused him before sunrise each day and sent him to run in the woods until noon. His endurance is now such that he needs to stop only once in that span of time, and Ontasaga tells me that he covers a longer distance than any of his peers. To develop their minds, the boys are required to be aware of nature as they run, familiarizing themselves with the creatures of the night as they seek shelter in the first light of dawn, observing the ways of birds and insects, and taking note of plants and their habitats.

In recent months, Oserohkoton and his cohort have been learning wrestling and self-defense, as well as their responsibilities in accordance with the Kaianereh'ko:wa, or Great Law of Peace, the origin of which I explained in an early letter. This law, taught through symbols by the women, and in practice by the men, is central to the governance of the Mohawk and other Iroquois nations. It contains great wisdom, Étienne, for its central tenet is respect. It recognizes the individuality of each person, but also the importance of working with and for others. A young warrior, in particular, must learn to accept the reality of his responsibilities, which starts with knowing what respect is. Only then can he respect himself, and move on to living the truth of his life as a man and a warrior, in which his primary goal is to render service to his people. How perfectly this echoes our order's concept of becoming 'a man for others!'

Thus progresses my most promising neophyte toward his destiny. I have no doubt that he will influence history in some way.

May you and our family continue to prosper in the light of God's love.

Vincent, S.J.

LETTER TWELVE

NEW FRANCE

(THIRTY-ONE MONTHS LATER)

Kahnawake, the 21ˢᵗ day of July, 1713

It has been almost three years since we last communicated, dear brother. Distance and time have a way of diluting urgency, but not love or concern. I read your letter received several weeks ago with great interest, and hasten to congratulate you and Marie-Céleste on the birth of another son, who must now be almost a year old. Two items in your letter gave me particular pleasure: first, that the little newcomer is named Henri in honor of our father; and, second, that you and Mother have been re-reading my early letters, and introducing not only Marie-Céleste but the twins to my accounts of life here in the New World. At almost six, they no doubt find them as fascinating as Perrault's fairy stories!

News has lately come to hand that a treaty ending the seemingly interminable war—eleven terrible years of loss and suffering—was signed in the spring, a cause for thankfulness, certainly, but also for mourning the lives so wantonly lost and bodies so savagely injured.

The ripples of peace reached our shores sometime before the official end to the war. Last year, observing signs that the hostilities that had for so long disrupted their valued trade with the English and Dutch were diminishing, our Mohawks sent a delegation of chiefs to Albany to 'bury the hatchet.' Oserohkoton, who is being groomed for chiefdom, accompanied them. These negotiations opened the way for the Dutch, acting on behalf of Reverend John Williams, to resume their attempts to redeem the minister's daughter, Eunice. Her father, greatly distressed at the news that she has married not only a 'savage' but a Catholic, was determined to renew his efforts to reclaim her. Having received Governor Vaudreuil's permission to meet with the girl, now sixteen, John Schuyler, the chief negotiator, arrived at Kahnawake in May. The meeting was to take place in the presence of Father Cholonec, who explained to Schuyler that he had done all he could to dissuade her from the marriage, and had only capitulated when she and her Mohawk sweetheart said they would live together whether or not he consented to perform the ceremony.

At the meeting, she, having long since forgotten her mother tongue, required a translator with knowledge of French, English (the language used by Schuyler), and Mohawk, a role that I was most willing to undertake. We had anticipated seeing her alone, and were disconcerted when she arrived accompanied by her husband, a young Mohawk by the name of François Xavier Arosen. Their demeanor, particularly hers, was one of unwavering resoluteness. Our fervent entreaties—think of your father's sorrow; your family longs for your return; will you not go to Deerfield just for a visit?—were met with stony silence. It was only when Schuyler accused her of heartless and unreasonable behavior that her husband let fall a revealing remark to the effect that she would have considered a visit if her father had not remarried. As in the case of Edmund Rice, this father, too, must bear the sorrowful burden of a child's rejection.

I seldom see Oserohkoton now that, at sixteen, he has reached man's status. When not away on hunting or fishing expeditions, he is increasingly called upon to accompany bands of Mohawk who join with their old enemies, the Abenakis, in forays against the English. Because the terms of the treaty that ended Queen Anne's War ignored the interests of the Indians, English settlers continue to encroach on Abenaki territory, which naturally has given rise to tremendous resentment.

By all accounts, Oserohkoton is fearless in confronting the enemy, but on a recent occasion he sought me out after one such expedition. He was clearly distressed, and told me that he had killed a man—not just a man, but an Englishman and therefore a blood brother.

. Feeling his pain, I hesitated for some time before replying.

"My son, in this imperfect world, the duty of a warrior is to fight on behalf of his people."

"But Father," he said, "for the honor of our clan, I was forced to take his scalp." Then, barely audibly, he added, "It was the most horrible thing I have ever done, and yet ... my heart exulted."

How to counsel him, Étienne, this young man, this boy, who is so precious in my sight? It seems bloodlust is fundamental to the human condition, and you will know only too well how it can overcome the most temperate of men. Aware that the elders exhort young warriors at the time of their initiation not to kill in anger and to maintain an inner calm even in the heat of battle, I reminded Oserohkoton of this.

"To avoid suffering such as you now experience, my son, it will be necessary to pray every day for the strength to master such base emotions. This I know you can do, with God's help, and that of Saint Hubert and your *manitou*."

He sat for some time, head bowed. Then, rising, he gazed at me, nodded slightly, and silently left the room.

"Thou shalt not kill." Will mankind ever find peace on this earth?

At the end of last year, I received the parcel of books you so kindly sent me. The wisdom they embody has brought me enlightenment and consolation. You may recall, Étienne, that some years ago, after my sojourn among the Huron, I was beset by doubts. When I sat in contemplation beside the river after my conversation with Father d'Avaugour, these words of an early Father ran remorselessly in my consciousness: "Where we sought to bring God's love and redemption we brought destruction and suffering." The mists rising from the water awakened memories of the wraiths that arose out of my fever so many years ago, setting me on the path to which Divine Providence had guided me, and from which I had never wavered until my visit to the Lorette mission. I could not mistrust the sanctity of those extraordinary men whose courage and devotion had inspired me to follow them in the service of Christ. To their everlasting glory, in the midst of pestilence and death, they were steadfast in their ardent desire to extend His kingdom through baptism. But I have come to understand that here at Kahnawake my soul will not find peace. Thus, when Father Cholonec received a directive from our superior in Québec assigning me to our mission at Kaskaskia in the territory of Illinois, I received the news with gratitude. I depart next spring, in my forty-third year. My work with Oserohkoton is done, and I must go where God draws me. If it is His will, you may receive news of me, but be prepared, dear brother, to accept that this missive could be my last.

I bid farewell with the words of Saint Ignatius: "I implore God to grant us all the grace to know His holy will and to accomplish it perfectly." May He ever hold you and our family in His embrace.

Yours in Christ,

Vincent, S.J.

New France and New England

This, then, is what the future held for the seven-year-old boy who awoke in the house on Powder Hill on that fateful August morning so long ago. It is as well that his mother has had no news of him, for the dreams she cherished are transformed into nightmares. That he and Silas, her beloved sons, are becoming leaders among the savages who killed their brother would be beyond her wildest imaginings. That they are not only savages but Papists would break her heart.

But Oserohkoton is content in the life that Fate thrust upon him, a life of service to his people. Despite his youth, he is often included when matters of importance to the tribe are to be weighed and decisions taken. It may be that, in 1715, he is at Onondaga as an observer when the Grand Council admits the Tuscaroras as the sixth nation of the Iroquois Confederacy. Perhaps, because of his eloquence, he accompanies the chiefs who journey to Québec to offer condolences to the French when King Louis XIV dies in 1717. Certain it is that throughout the years he grows in wisdom and judgment, qualities that manifest particularly in his compassion toward prisoners, who traditionally were often burnt alive if they did not accept adoption.

His memories of life as an English boy lie far beneath the surface of his consciousness, until one day when Ontasaga returns from a journey that took him through Chauncy, now renamed Westborough. He tells Oserohkoton that he was on the outskirts of the town when he passed a house beside a spring where a man was sitting, staring into its depths. "He looked up as I approached, and gazed at me with such horror before fleeing that I had difficulty moving from where I stood. My son," he says, "it was your cousin Ashur, who recognized me from the time he was captured."

Ashur! Alive! Perhaps, then, other members of his family are as well. This unexpected connection to his English roots has come at a poignant time, for he is soon to be married. His wife-to-be is Catherine Osennehawe, a Christian Mohawk, who will wish to honor his ancestors, especially if they have children. He vows to travel to the place of his birth as soon as an opportunity arises.

Two years later, such is his standing as a negotiator in both New France and New England that he receives an invitation from Governor Belcher of Massachusetts to visit him at the Boston State House. Having forgotten the language he spoke as a child, he sets out in company with John Tarbell, who has retained a serviceable knowledge of English since his capture, and will act as interpreter.

Having never measured time in the white man's way, he is unaware that Fate has brought him to the place of his birth on the date of his birth forty-three years later. When they reach the town, Thomas welcomes his nephew and John to his new home not far from the flax fields. He tells Oserohkoton that his parents died many years ago, and, to his nephew's profound disappointment, that Ashur has left the house his father built for him in Westborough, and moved to another community.

No longer a hamlet, the town is now home to more than a hundred families. Its leading citizens treat the two Mohawks as celebrities, take them to Powder Hill for an official ceremony in the meeting house, which stands on land donated by Edmund Rice and David Maynard's family. On the way, Oserohkoton catches a glimpse of his old home, barely visible behind a thicket of wild shrubs and tall grass. When the ceremony is over, he begs leave of his hosts to go alone to the place where he was born.

The house is derelict. The door, hanging by one hinge, creaks in the afternoon breeze. As he steps over the threshold, he sees, as if it were yesterday, his father carrying four-year-old Timothy on his back as the family returns from Sunday worship at the Marlborough meeting house six miles distant. So vivid is the image that he expects to smell the beans and ham that his mother has left simmering on the hearth. Instead, all about him is the odor of decay, and an owl blinks at him from the top of the ladder that he scrambled down so long ago. A flood of memories rises from the dark and the dust: his stern father with an arm around his wife's waist, courteously bargaining with a peddler for a primer so that his children might learn to read, and for colored threads needed to complete Dinah's sampler; his mother churning butter amid the aroma of baking apples; Silas, tongue between teeth, fashioning a corn-husk doll for Huldah, embellishing it with round eyes, a wobbly mouth, and a scrap of red yarn for a scarf. Overwhelmed, he seeks the solace of sunlight, makes his way to the place where his mother's vegetable garden used to be. There, amid lonely squash plants and corn stalks struggling in a wilderness of weeds, he feels her presence acutely. In the shadow of a bush at the back perimeter, beside two mysterious cairns of stones, he finds a wooden cross. Dropping to his knees, he traces the inscription with his finger. Like bubbles in a bog, the meanings of the letters and numbers his mother taught him ooze up through the sediment of time into his consciousness. He spells out: M-O-S-E-S—R-I-C-E, M-a-r-c-h—1-7-0-3—O-c-t-o-b-e-r—1-7-0-4 . . . the baby brother he hardly knew, dead two months after he and his brothers were captured. O that he could comfort his father and mother! Only now does he understand the depth of their suffering.

As if in a trance, he retraces the path that he and his father and brothers took on the morning that changed his life, past the Maynard property and along the widened track to the flax field. Homesteads dot the previously empty wilderness. His uncle's old garrison house is now a tavern, but the small hill where Ontasaga and his band were concealed remains unchanged. How long he stands in contemplation on its summit he does not know. At last, in the waning light, his uncle and John Tarbell come in search of him. Before returning home, they make a detour-- Thomas takes him to where Nahor was buried in the southern corner of what has become the town's cemetery. Overcome, Oserohkoton asks to be left to find his way back to his uncle's house. It is long after dark when he leaves Grave Plain.

Georgian Bay, New France

The calm expanse of the lake draws the darkness from Father Vincent's soul. Moment follows serene moment of vivid awareness: the splash of a fish, a bird's call, shining drops falling from the blade of his paddle, the gleaming backs of his companions. At night, firelit faces, a simple meal eaten in silence, lapping water and rustling leaves, moonlit.

After several days, a canoe appears as they leave their camp site. Two men signal that they come in peace. They are Illini, and communication is difficult but not impossible, Father Vincent and the Mohawks having some knowledge of Algonquin, the strangers' language. Their chief is dying, they say. He is a Christian, and his soul is in torment because there is no priest to perform the last rites. Will the Black Robe accompany them so that their chief can die in peace? Their settlement is at a distance of two days by water.

Anxious to be of service, Father Vincent consults with the Mohawk who have brought him this far. After debating among themselves, they say they must return to Kahnawake in time to prepare for the winter, and fear that any delay would not allow them to provide for their people; whereupon the Illini indicate that they are willing to convey the Black Robe to his destination, as the route is well known to them. The matter being settled in this manner, Father Vincent bids farewell to his Mohawk companions, and joins the Illini in their canoe.

Their community of about sixty people is on an island hidden among a myriad others. He learns that they had fled the depredations of the Seneca some months before, and that there are twenty-two Christians among them.

As he sets foot on the island, the Black Robe is received with joy by Christians and heathens alike, for their chief is beloved by all. They lead the priest to a bark shelter where women pray in the shadows beyond the

motionless body of the chief. Kneeling beside the man, Father Vincent
sees his eyes flicker open, then briefly gleam with the light of recognition.
He asks the people if they would be willing to lay the chief in a clearing
so that all may join in prayer about him. Reverently, four men carry him
on a beaver robe. There, with alder bushes as a sanctuary and a tall cedar
for a steeple, the old chief's people gather round him. As they form a circle,
an imposing figure appears—a man in the clothes of a woman—who is
respectfully given a place among them. Father Vincent senses the inner
peace that emanates from him, and welcomes his presence.

TOURAINE, FRANCE

It is twenty-three years since Aurélie de Surville died, her heart still longing for news, any news, of her eldest son. Attempting to ease his mother's yearning, over the years Étienne has written to the Jesuit superiors in Paris and Québec, and French officials in New France, to no avail. From the replies he receives, it is clear that whether alive or dead, his brother has vanished without trace.

His mother's last words echo in his memory: "Never forget, him, Étienne, dear son." Vincent's letters have long lain unread, but today the leather bag in which they are stored is on his knees as he sits by the fire in the library. Although it is summer, he feels cold. Now in his sixty-sixth year, the effects of his injury are taking their toll, and he has handed over the running of the estate to his younger son, Henri, a stalwart man in his thirties, with the shrewd business sense that characterized his namesake, Étienne's father.

As he pores over the letters, enthralled as if reading them for the first time, his wife enters, places a hand on his shoulder. "The courier has just delivered this, Étienne. It is from New France."

LETTER THIRTEEN

New France

Kahnawake, the 16th day of September, 1741

Dear Father,

My duties in the service of M. Hocquart prevented me from coming earlier to Kahnawake, which I regret because I know how eager you are to learn what became of your beloved brother. As the Intendant's office oversees justice, in addition to finance and policing, I have been much occupied in educating myself during the past year, and it is only now that an occasion has arisen allowing me to visit the mission.

How strange it is to be in the place that has gripped my imagination since childhood! As you know, Uncle Vincent's accounts of this settlement more than thirty years ago captivated me from the time I could read, and I thank you for allowing me access to them for they greatly enriched my understanding. As is to be expected, much has changed at Kahnawake. French-style dwellings have replaced most of the longhouses, and a stone church stands in the place of the wooden one that was central to my uncle's life. The stone rectory remains, however, and I was much moved when I was shown the narrow cell that was home to Uncle Vincent while he served the people of Kahnawake..

On my arrival, I was warmly welcomed by Fathers Luc François Nau and Jacques Quintin de la Bretonnière, and I lost no time in enquiring whether they had any knowledge concerning my uncle. Having had notification of my visit, they had searched their records and were able to show me a short letter brought back to Kahnawake by the Mohawks who escorted him as far as Georgian Bay, from whence he was to make his way by water in company with a band of Indians from the territory of Illinois who undertook to conduct him to Kaskaskia. Here is a transcription of my uncle's words:

Georgian Bay on the Lake of the Hurons, June 1711

To my brothers in Christ at the Mission of Sault Saint Louis

Thanks be to God and the Holy Virgin, several arduous weeks by canoe along the Ottawa and French Rivers have brought us safely to this place. Before me lies an inland sea, vast as His compassion and grace. This outer journey is serving to clear away the dross that has for so long clouded the window of my soul. May God in his mercy guide my inner pilgrimage to a place of peace through surrender to His will.

Should it be in your power to convey a message to my family in Touraine, I beg you to assure them that they are ever in my prayers.

Your brother in Christ,

Vincent, S.J.

Nothing further was heard until three years later, when a missionary, returning from Illinois to Québec, mentioned to the Jesuit superior that my uncle had never arrived at Kaskaskia, and that it was feared he had died at the hands of the Chickasaw or some other hostile tribe. This news much depressed my spirits, as I know it will yours, and I am thankful that my grandmother was spared this knowledge.

I sought to honor my uncle in prayer before the likeness of the holy Kateri Tekakwitha, which still graces the church, and the Fathers offered me comfort by relating what their predecessors and the Indians remembered of the good work he had accomplished. They, in turn, were interested in my account of Oserohkoton's arrival at Kahnawake as recorded by my uncle in his letters to you, and the English boy's journey to acceptance of our faith under Uncle Vincent's guidance. The Fathers told me that the young captive who came to the mission so many years ago (by my calculation, he is now in his forty-fourth year) is a greatly respected sachem among the Mohawk. Father Luc then offered to arrange a meeting with Oserohkoton at the council house. You can imagine with what eagerness I accompanied him thither at the appointed time.

We found Oserohkoton and his brother, Tannhahorens, who is also a sachem, seated outside the council longhouse, together with John Tarbell (his Indian name is beyond my ability to transcribe), who, having been taken captive at a more advanced age than the Rice brothers, has retained some knowledge of his native English. He served as interpreter, and although my fluency in that language is less than perfect, it was adequate for understanding John's simple translations.

Impressive in their dignity, the brothers rose to greet me most courteously, their blue eyes contrasting strangely with their skin, darkened by many years of sun and paint. My visit was well timed, for I learned that last month a son, baptized with the name Pierre, was born to Oserohkoton and his wife, Catherine Osennenhawe, and I was thus able to offer them my sincere congratulations.

Oserohkoton spoke of Father Vincent with deep respect, calling him 'my true father,' and emphasizing his wisdom and devotion to his faith. I said I was sorry to hear that he had disappeared before reaching Kaskaskia, whereupon Oserohkoton somewhat hesitantly confided that over the years, rumors had come to the ears of the Mohawk that there was a Black Robe living on one of the multitudinous islands in Lake Huron, and that he had often wondered whether the mysterious priest could be Father Vincent. I asked if he had ever considered going in search of my uncle, whereupon he explained that his duties as a sachem had not allowed him to be absent from the tribe for the extended time it would take to make such a journey, adding that nothing would give him greater pleasure than to see his old mentor again.

This exchange with Oserohkoton has given rise to profound emotions, father, not only the desire to go on a quest to find my uncle, or at least discover what became of him, but also to experience this strange land and its people more closely than is possible in Québec. Accordingly, I intend to ask for an extended leave of absence, and to determine whether Oserohkoton will accompany me on a journey to the Lake of the Hurons. There will doubtless be dangers, but there are no rewards without risks.

My official mission at Kahnawake is completed and I must return to Québec, where I shall mail this letter. Please convey my loving remembrance to my mother, and assure my sister and Henri of my loving thoughts.

Your respectful and devoted son,

Vincent

Georgian Bay

It is summer in Montréal when young Vincent and Oserohkoton, with John Tarbell as interpreter, set forth on their quest. After long weeks of paddling upstream on the Ottawa River, then downstream on the narrow Mattawa with its hazards of debris and fallen trees; after negotiating the seven-mile portage at La Vase that brought them to the French River, they at last reach the vast expanse of Georgian Bay on Lake Huron. At the mouth of the river they find an encampment of coureurs des bois, *who are preparing to undertake the same journey in reverse. From them they learn that in order to safely negotiate the bay, they must hug the northern coastline if they are to avoid being capsized by the squalls that come in from the west. From them they also learn that among the thousands of islands in the bay there is one that is regarded by the local Indians as having strong spiritual significance. They have not been there themselves, the fur trappers say, but the Hurons who live in a village a day's walk north know the area well.*

"We have heard of a Black Robe," says a Huron elder. "We have heard that he is to be found on an island that lies three days by canoe west of the sacred white cliffs. But the islands are as stars, so great is their number," he says, "and we in our travels have never seen him." He also warns them to be vigilant, for the Seneca, who are known for their aggressiveness, have on occasion been seen in the area.

On the long walk back to their canoe, Vincent and his companions discuss how they should proceed. They have little information to guide them and recognize the dangers of getting lost in the watery wilderness. Vincent has brought with him a brass compass that measures the sun's angle and also serves as a timepiece; while Oserohkoton says that he and John will take careful note of sun and stars, currents and landmarks, "so that we may find our way back to the French River."

Having had the foresight to replenish their supplies of pemmican and parched corn at the Huron settlement, the three travelers set forth. They paddle north for a half day, past limestone boulders and cliffs dotted with scrub pine, past bays and beaches overlooked by cedars. In the blazing light of noon, they round a headland. Before them are the sacred cliffs, unmistakable in their blinding whiteness. In awe, they still their paddles.

An hour later, they set a course due west, but soon realize that their journey will take more days than three because of the number of islands, big and small, that lie in their path. But they remain true to their western direction, resetting their course after every obstacle. At night, they light no fires and take turns keeping watch.

On the fifth day, they hear the call of a loon. Oserohkoton and John are immediately on the alert. They reach for the flintlocks they have brought with them. Before they have time to load, they see two canoes approaching swiftly from different directions. As they come nearer, Oserohkoton sees that they are not Seneca. He holds his hands above his head to show he is unarmed. "Friend," he says in both Mohawk and Algonquin, when the canoes are within hailing distance. "We seek the Black Robe."

"We are Illini," they reply. "We know where to find him. Follow us."

LETTER FOURTEEN

GEORGIAN BAY

Georgian Bay, the 12ᵗʰ day of August 1742

Étienne, my dear brother,

You will doubtless be astonished to receive a letter from me, but not more astonished than I am to be writing it. The paper that I brought from Kahnawake is sadly yellowed now, but the joy in my heart in communicating with you is such that I do not know where to start.

When I went to the beach on the island that has been my home for almost thirty years to greet the 'strangers' arriving in a canoe, and saw what to my bewildered imagination was my brother walking towards me, in company with my most beloved convert, I fell to my knees and covered my face fearing that a fever had entered my brain. But when two strong arms, one from either side, gently brought me to my feet, I ventured to open my eyes, whereupon my nephew threw his arms about me in a warm embrace, and Oserohkoton clasped my hands in his. I marvel that they knew me, for my black robe is long gone and I wear only its sash around my deerskin garments. Furthermore, my complexion is much darkened from exposure to the elements, a beard conceals my crucifix, and a braid adds to my disguise.

But I am forgetting that you are in ignorance as to how I found myself on an island. In brief, after leaving Kahnawake, and while crossing Lake Huron on my way to the Kaskaskia mission in the territory of Illinois, two Indians in a canoe intercepted the craft in which I was traveling with my Mohawk escorts. The strangers were Illini, natives of that territory, who beseeched me to go with them, as their chief, a Christian, was dying, and there was no priest to perform the last rites. I could not ignore such an appeal. As my Mohawk companions were anxious to return to Kahnawake to participate in preparations for winter, they discussed my onward journey with the Illini, who gave their assurances that they would convey me to Kaskaskia.

This was not to be. Some days after the chief's death, when I was ready to continue my journey, six young warriors who had ventured forth in search of news concerning Kaskaskia, returned to the island not only with news, but with wives. They said they had learned at neighboring settlements that the mission was in the throes of a plague that had already killed hundreds. Furthermore, they had on several occasions barely eluded hostile tribes intent on taking captives, whereupon the men who were to escort me to Kaskaskia refused to leave the island.

I was concerned that I was not fulfilling my assigned mission, but, believing the delay to be temporary, I resolved to learn what I could and to make myself useful to the small community. There was indeed much to be learned and done, for the people had only a few months before arrived on the island and had yet to accustom themselves to their changed circumstances. Pines, oaks, low-growing juniper and reeds provided material for dwellings, but there were few deer and beaver, and although fish, duck and berries were plentiful, the people were still having to draw on supplies they had brought with them while they sought suitable places to grow corn.

As my small flock looked to me not only for spiritual guidance but for help with bodily ailments, I set about educating myself as to the properties of available plants against the day when my medical supplies should be exhausted. In this, it is doubtful I would have succeeded without the help of a man in woman's dress who joined the prayer circle when the chief died. His name is Quanopin, and he is a man of remarkable gifts, Étienne. In many societies, including ours, he would be reviled, yet among the Illini he is revered as a two-spirit person who can see into the hearts of both men and women. He has told me that in his tribe, and in many others, clan mothers closely observe young children. If they are seen to have both masculine and feminine traits, their families and the community rejoice, for such people are valued not only for their spiritual gifts, but for their artistic abilities and willingness to work hard. Quanopin interprets his people's dreams and determines what is troubling their spirits, but he has also acquired much knowledge concerning the natural world, and how it may best serve his people. That is his primary and selfless aim, which, on occasion, has necessitated his taking up arms in their defense. Most notably, he is at peace within himself.

With winter approaching, I recognized the need to build some sort of shelter to serve as a place of worship. My Christians were most diligent in their help, but on one occasion, when I found myself working alone, God spoke to me. I knew then that it was His will that had brought me to this island so that I could serve Him in humility and with love, untroubled by violence, avarice, and dogma. I knew that here, in purity of faith, my soul would be healed in service to these people who had suffered so greatly. Those who were not Christian believed in a Master of Life who directs all creation, but in their honesty, loyalty and human kindness, I saw them as imbued with the spirit of Christ, whether or not they were baptized.

Over the years, many children were born. Unlike the early missionaries, I baptized none without the knowledge and consent of their parents. Seeing that I did not seek to persuade them away from their beliefs, some asked to be instructed in our faith. When I no longer had hosts for the Eucharist, Quanopin showed me how to fashion small wafers from the pollen of cattails, and pure water took the place of wine, both of which elements of the Mass I consecrated to His glory.

By the time my nephew and Oserohkoton arrived, a number of families had moved farther afield, for the island could not sustain a large population; and some elders had risked returning to Kaskaskia, wishing to be buried with their ancestors. While I had never given thought to such a possibility for myself, when I experienced the joy of speaking my native language with Vincent my heart was drawn to the land of my birth and to those I have ever held most dear. We have spent many hours talking about France, Touraine and, most of all, our beloved family and home. Your son has importuned me to return with him, and for weeks my heart has been torn. To see you again and to live out the remainder of our lives together in Touraine—ah, Étienne, there could be no greater blessing. Tormented in spirit, I have beseeched God for guidance. Last night, as I stood outside our modest church in the dark silence of a starless night, I received my answer: To His everlasting glory, I shall rejoice in devoting my last days to serving these people whose lives have been devastated by the presence of our race.

Vincent and Oserohkoton depart tomorrow, bearing this letter. To you, my dear brother, whose image is before me as I write these words, I do not bid farewell, for you are as one with me.

My soul is at peace.

Praise be to God.

Vincent, S.J.

ADDENDA

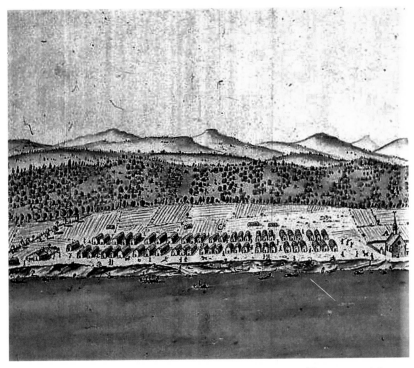

View of Kahnawake in the mid-eighteenth century. Drawing with
ink and watercolors, mid-eighteenth century artist unknown. Cliché
Bibliothèque nationale de France; Cabinet des Estampes, Paris.

AFTERWORD

Account of the Rice boys' abduction by Reverend Ebenezer Parkman, the first minister of Westborough.

FOUR RICES CAPTIVATED

On Aug. 8th, in the year 1704, at the south part of Marlboro', then called Chauncy, now Westboro', as Several Persons were busy in spreading Flax, on a plain about fourscore rods from the House of Mr. Thomas Rice (who was for several years Representative for Marlboro') and a number of Boys with them two of which were sons of the said Mr. Thomas Rice; & three others, sons of Mr. Edmund Rice; Seven, some say Ten, Indians, suddenly rushed down a woody Hill close by, and Seizing and scalping the least of the Boys, (one of ye three last mentioned, & about five years old) they took the other four captive, the two sons of Mr. Thomas Rice, Namely Asher and Adonijah, the oldest about 10, the other about 8 years; and the other two of Mr. Edmund Rice, of about 9 & 7, their Names, Silas and Timothy; and carryd them away to Canada; those persons who were spreading Flax, escaping to the House safely.

Asher, in about four years, returned, being redeemed by his Father. This was bro't about by the kind Mediation of the Rev. Mr. Lydius, then Minister of Albany. [It is a little observable, that when the old Indian sachem, Ountassogo (Ontasaga) (the Chief of the Cagnawagas at the Conference wth. Govr. Belcher at Deerfield) made a Visit to Boston, & stop'd a while here in this Town, the forementioned Asher Saw him and knew him to be one of those Indians, who rushd down the Hill, as above, when the Children were captivated.] This Mr. Asher Rice is now living in Spencer. His Brother Adonijah grew up in Canada; but marryd first a French, afterwards a Dutch woman; settled in Husbandry, on some Land a little way from Montreal, on the North Side of the great River; has a good Farm there for many Years, as we have been certifyd; and he is very probably, now living there at this Day.

As to the two other boys, Silas and Timothy, (sons of M^r· Edmund Rice aforesaid) we have had credible Information from time to time, yt they mixd with the Indians; lost their Mother Tongue; had indian Wives, & Children by them and liv'd at Cagnawaga. Their Friends among us had news of them not long since, that they were then alive; so that they may be in all probability there still.

But respecting Timothy, the younger of them, who is by much the most noticeable, the Acc^{ts}. we have always had, have represented him, as having been for many Years, the Third of the Six Chiefs of that Tribe before mentioned. This Advancem^t I understand was upon the Death of his Master, or Foster-Father, who adopted him to be his son, instead of a son which he, the former Chief, had lost. But however, Timothy had much recommended himself to the Indians by his own superior Talents; his Penetration, Courage, strength & warlike spirit; for which he was much celebrated. This was evident to me when in Conversation with the late Mohawk Sachem Hendrick & M^r. Kellogg, at the Time of their being in the Massachusetts; and his Name was among them the same that we had known him by, viz.

OUGHTZORONGOUGHTON.

—But he himself, in process of time, came to see us.

By the Interposition of Col. Lydius, & ye Captain Tarbel (who was carryd away from Groton) a Letter was sent me, bearing date July 23, 1740, which certifyd that if one of their Brethren here, would go up to Albany, & be there at a Time specify'd, they would meet him there; & that One of them at least, would come hither to visit their Friends in New England. This Proposal was readily comply'd with and it succeeded. For the Chief abovesaid came hither. The said M^r. Tarbell came also with him as an Interpreter & Companion. They arrived here Sept. 15th. They view'd the House where M^r. Rice dwelt, & the Place from whence the Children above spoke of, were captivated; of both which he retained a clear Remembrance; as he did likewise of Several elderly Persons who were then living; tho' he had forgot our Language. His Excell^cy Govr. Belcher sent for them; who accordingly waited on him at Boston. They visited also Tarbels Relations at Groton; and then returned to us in their Way back to Albany & Canada.

Col. Lydius, when at Boston a while ago, Said this Rice was the Chief who made the Speech to Genl. Gage (which we had in our public Prints) in behalf of ye Cagnawaga's, Soon after the Reduction of Montreal. This last may be further enquired into; but the rest which I have here writ, is from good Authority, as I humbly Suppose. In particular as to the Captivating; three Persons who were Present, & escap'd the Indians Hands, as abovesaid, are now alive, and testifie to this Acc^t.

I am &c.

EB^R. PARKMAN

Westboro
May 1769

છ જી

In the build-up to the American Revolution, Samuel Adams and Joseph Warren of the Committee of Correspondence in Boston received a letter from Captain John Brown in Montreal in which he put forward the possibility that the Indians of that region might be persuaded to ally themselves with the Americans and take up arms against the British.

Extract from *The Tribe of the Great White Chiefs*, by Margaret Erskine:

"Two men from the New Hampshire Grants accompanied me over the Lakes. The one an old Indian hunter, acquainted with the St. François Indians and their language; the other was a captive many years among the Caughnawaga (Kahnawake) Indians, which is the principal of all the Canadian Six Nations and western tribes of Indians, whom I sent to inquire and search out any intrigues carrying on among them. These men have this minute returned, and report that they were very kindly received by the Caughnawaga Indians with whom they tarried several days.

"The Indians say they have been repeatedly applied to, and requested to join with the King's Troops to fight Boston, but they have peremptorily refused, and still intend to refuse. They are very simple, politick people, and say that if they are obliged, for their own safety, to take up arms on either side, that they shall take part on the side of their brethren in New England; *all the chiefs of the Caughnawaga tribe being of English extraction, captivated in their infancy.*" (Author's italics.)

According to Erskine, Oserohkoton "apparently was the chief who led the Caughnawagas when Montreal fell during the French and Indian War and Gov. the Marquis de Vaudreuil surrendered all of Canada to Great Britain in 1760. In 1775 he was still alive and was probably one of the chiefs Capt. Brown's emissaries talked to. He died in September 1777."

ACKNOWLEDGMENTS

Before paying tribute to the stalwart supporters who have stood by me in the thirty-year marathon of writing this story, I wish to acknowledge the role of the internet, which, as my manuscript neared completion, most fortuitously directed me into the orbit of Linda McCullough Moore. With gracious but insistent coaxing, backed by the insights and enthusiasm of the remarkable writers in her manuscript group, Linda urged me over the finish line. As a first-time author, I could not have wished for a kinder and more professional introduction to the daunting world of publishing. I also had the good fortune to benefit from the discernment of Sarah Halper, Fran Kidder and Libby Maxey, who meticulously reviewed my work and encouraged me to add a dimension that brought depth and heart to the story. I am most grateful to them all, as well as to Steve Strimer and his team at Levellers Press, who guided the project to completion with consideration and attention to detail.

Warm thanks, too, to my early editors, Marion Walker and Sophy Burnham, and more recent editor, Holly Moore, who moved the manuscript forward with their substantive comments on content and style; and to James Spencer and his group of creative writers at the Northampton Senior Center, whose positive and perceptive assessments helped me to establish a core of self-confidence.

My earliest readers, Sandy and Suzanne Renna, and Kenneth Henderson, kept me on course with their enthusiasm and regular check-ins; while Kristina Allen, Dennis Callahan, Jan Cannon, Kelley Crisp, Coni Douglas, Prunella Fiddian-Green, grandson Jordan Hensley, and daughters-in-law Josephine and Larissa Hensley, and Karen Thomas, took time out of their busy lives to read my manuscript and contribute their valuable perspectives. I am most grateful to each one of them.

Along the way, cheerleaders buoyed flagging spirits and put forward ideas to overcome writer's block. Jules Seltzer, besides introducing me to the movie "Black Robe," has maintained a steady interest in the story's progress; at a crucial point, my Westborough booster group, "The Prodigal Daughters," headed by Josephine Hensley, provided much-needed direction and encouragement; Richard and Candace Carlisle not only read an early version of my story, but shared with me their enthusiasm for history and their knowledge of Georgian Bay; and, in a final flourish, Judith Pool's coterie of francophiles kept the tricolor flying as publication became more than just a possibility. I salute and thank them all!

I am particularly grateful to anthropologist Ralph Rataul of the State Museum of New York for his willingness to read my manuscript, and for validating my depiction of Mohawk culture; and to my former colleagues on the board of the Westborough Historical Society, whose dedication to preserving the history of the town that once was home to the Rice boys inspired me to complete their story.

In my research, *On the Beaten Path: Westborough, Massachusetts,* by Kristina Nilson Allen, provided the earliest nugget of information—Reverend Ebenezer Parkman's account of the Rice boys' capture (see Afterword); and two books in particular were indispensable sources of information: *The Unredeemed Captive,* by John Demos, and *Captors and Captives,* by Evan Haefeli and Kevin Sweeney. I am indebted to them, and to the *Relations* of the early Jesuit missionaries, for much of the historical basis of the narrative.

To my sister, Marian Lucas, and niece, Vivienne Barbadoro, I offer my deep appreciation for their clear-sighted critiques and unflagging support, so lovingly given; and I am at a loss for words to adequately thank our children, Kenton, Lester, Julia and Mark, whose talents, unstinting encouragement and love shaped this journey. Sharing it with them, and with Peter, has been my greatest joy.

ങ ഇ

GLOSSARY

Ague: a fever (often malaria) marked by paroxysms of chills

Bastinado: a beating with a stick

Brimstone: sulphur

Cairn: a mound of stones, often built as a memorial

Calumet: ceremonial pipe

Catechumen: convert still learning the catechism and therefore not yet baptized

Canonical hours: seven prayer times appointed for each day by canon law

Cinchona: source of quinine, brought from Peru by Jesuits in the 17th century

Confrère: fellow priest

Coureurs des bois: fur traders

Diligence: stage coach

Drapeaux d'ordonnance: regimental colors

Forecastle: the part of a vessel at the bow comprising the crew's quarters and storage area

Habitants: inhabitants, residents

Hôtel-Dieu: hospital

In extremis: at the point of death

Laudanum: an alcoholic solution containing morphine, prepared from opium and formerly used as a narcotic painkiller.

Lung fever: pneumonia

Mal de mer: seasickness

Matelots: sailors

Mêlée: free-for-all

Neophyte: recently baptized Christian

Nostrum: a medicine, especially one that is not considered effective, prepared by an unqualified person

Palisade: a fence or wall made from wooden stakes or tree trunks and used as a defensive enclosure

Prie-dieu: prayer stool

Relations: *The Jesuit Relations* were annual reports sent by Jesuit missionaries to their superiors regarding progress in converting Native American tribes to Christianity

Rubeola: measles

Sachem: a member of the governing body of the League of the Iroquois

S.J.: Society of Jesus

Tare: Weed

Theriac: a cure-all concoction of treacle, spices and a variety of exotic ingredients

BIBLIOGRAPHY

Allen, Kristina Nilson, *On the Beaten Path*: Westborough, Massachusetts, 1984

Bill, Dr. Joseph Howland, *Notes on Arrow Wounds* (Internet)

Blanchard, David S., *Kahnawake: A Historical Sketch* (Kanien'kehaka Raotitiohkwa Cultural Center)

Bonaparte, Darren, *The First Families of Akwesasne*

Catholic Encyclopedia

Chauchetière, Claude, *La Narration de la Mission du Sault*

Colden, Cadwallader, *Founding Fathers*

Coleman, Emma Lewis, *New England Captives Carried to Canada*

DeForest, Heman Packard, *The History of Westborough*, 1891

Demos, John, *The Unredeemed Captive*, Alfred A. Knopf, New York, 1994

Devine, E.J., S.J., *Historic Caughnawaga*, Messenger Press, Montreal 1922

Dictionary of Canadian Biography

Encyclopedia of American Indian History

Forbes, Harriette Merrifield, *The 100th Town—Westboro*, MA 1717–1817, 1889

Gale Encyclopedia of Native American Tribes

Haefeli, Evan & Sweeney, Kevin, *Captors and Captives: The 1704 Indian Raid on Deerfield*

Handbook of North American Indians

History Channel: Battle of Blenheim 1704 (2004)

Hollis, Christopher, *The Jesuits: A History*

Jesuit Relations, The: *Natives and Missionaries in Seventeenth Century North America*, Allan Greer Editor

Johnson, Bruce E., *Forgotten Founders*

Kimball, Everett, *The Public Life of Joseph Dudley: A Study of the Colonial Policy of the Stuarts in New England*

Parkman, Rev. Ebenezer, *The Story of the Rice Boys* (1769)

Parkman, Francis, *The Jesuits in North America*, University Press, John Wilson & Son, Cambridge, MA

Ramage Family History (Internet)

Rootsweb.com: Family Finder

Seton, Julia M., *The Gospel of the Red Man*

Turner, Frederick W., *The Portable North American Indian Reader*, Penguin Books

Taylor & Sturtevant, *The Native Americans: The Indigenous People of North America*

Williams, Rev. John, *The Redeemed Captive Returning to Zion*

Williams, Walter L., *The Spirit and the Flesh: Sexual Diversity in American Indian Culture*